Nursing and Malpractice Risks
Understanding the Law

Fourth Edition

WESTERN® SCHOOLS

By
Barbara Youngberg, BSN, MSW, JD, FASHRM

![Western Schools logo] P.O. Box 1930
Brockton, MA 02303
WESTERN SCHOOLS 1-800-438-8888

ABOUT THE AUTHOR

Barbara Youngberg, BSN, MSW, JD, FASHRM, is the Director of Insurance Risk and Clinical Quality Management for University Hospital Consortium, which is an alliance of 84 teaching hospitals across the country. Her duties include risk management and clinical quality and legal consulting for member organizations.

Research Contributors for the 4th Edition, Michele Stone and Barbara Giardino.

ABOUT THE SUBJECT MATTER REVIEWER

Modesta S. Orque, RN, MPH, EdD, JD, is a solo practicing attorney in San Francisco, CA. She has also conducted well-received seminars to nurses in California on the prevention of malpractice. Ms. Orque has served as counsel at the Department of Corporations in the area of the regulation of managed care plans of California and worked as a nurse consultant for the Childhood Lead Poisoning Prevention Branch of the California Department of Health Services. She has also served as the Director of Public Health Nursing of the Fresno California County Health Department and has taught public health nursing for 10 years in two baccalaureate nursing programs in California. Modesta directed the Stroke Resocialization Program of the California Medical Association as well as establishing a notable reputation as a scholar, speaker, writer and leader in the area of cross-cultural health care delivery. Included in her writing accomplishments is the award-winning book, *Ethnic Nursing Care; A Multicultural Approach,* St. Louis, The C.V. Mosby Co. 1983.

Copy Editor: Jackie Bonham, RN, MSN

Indexer: Sylvia Coates

Typesetter: Kathy Johnson

ISBN 1-57801-054-3

IMPORTANT: Read these instructions *BEFORE* proceeding!

Enclosed with your course book you will find the FasTrax® answer sheet. Use this form to answer all the final exam questions that appear in this course book. If you are completing more than one course, be sure to write your answers on the appropriate answer sheet. Full instructions and complete grading details are printed on the FasTrax instruction sheet, also enclosed with your order. Please review them before starting. *If you are mailing your answer sheet(s) to Western Schools, we recommend you make a copy as a backup.*

ABOUT THIS COURSE

A "Pretest" is provided with each course to test your current knowledge base regarding the subject matter contained within this course. Your "Final Exam" is a multiple choice examination. **You will find the exam questions at the end of each chapter.**

In the event the course has less than 100 questions, leave the remaining answer boxes on the FasTrax answer sheet blank. **Use a <u>black pen</u> to fill in your answer sheet.**

A PASSING SCORE

You must score 70% or better in order to pass this course and receive your Certificate of Completion. Should you fail to achieve the required score, we will send you an additional FasTrax answer sheet so that you may make a second attempt to pass the course. Western Schools will allow you three chances to pass the same course...*at no extra charge!* After three failed attempts to pass the same course, your file will be closed.

RECORDING YOUR HOURS

Please monitor the time it takes to complete this course using the handy log sheet on the other side of this page. See below for transferring study hours to the course evaluation.

COURSE EVALUATIONS

In this course book you will find a short evaluation about the course you are soon to complete. This information is vital to providing the school with feedback on this course. The course evaluation answer section is in the lower right hand corner of the FasTrax answer sheet marked "Evaluation" with answers marked 1–25. Your answers are important to us, please take five minutes to complete the evaluation.

On the back of the FasTrax instruction sheet there is additional space to make any comments about the course, the school, and suggested new curriculum. Please mail the FasTrax instruction sheet, with your comments, back to Western Schools in the envelope provided with your course order.

TRANSFERRING STUDY TIME

Upon completion of the course, transfer the total study time from your log sheet to question #25 in the Course Evaluation. The answers will be in ranges, please choose the proper hour range that best represents your study time. You MUST log your study time under question #25 on the course evaluation.

EXTENSIONS

You have 2 years from the date of enrollment to complete this course. A six (6) month extension may be purchased. If after 30 months from the original enrollment date you do not complete the course, *your file will be closed and no certificate can be issued.*

CHANGE OF ADDRESS?

In the event you have moved during the completion of this course please call our student services department at 1-800-618-1670 and we will update your file.

A GUARANTEE YOU'LL GIVE HIGH HONORS TO

If any continuing education course fails to meet your expectations or if you are not satisfied in any manner, for any reason, you may return it for an exchange or a refund (less shipping and handling) within 30 days. Software, video and audio courses must be returned unopened.

Thank you for enrolling at Western Schools!

WESTERN SCHOOLS
P.O. Box 1930
Brockton, MA 02303
(800) 438-8888
www.westernschools.com

Nursing and Malpractice Risks: Understanding the Law

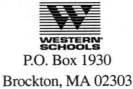

WESTERN
SCHOOLS

P.O. Box 1930
Brockton, MA 02303

Please use this log to total the number of hours you spend reading the text and taking the final examination (use 50-min hours).

Date	Hours Spent
_____	_____
_____	_____
_____	_____
_____	_____
_____	_____
_____	_____
_____	_____
_____	_____
_____	_____
_____	_____
_____	_____
_____	_____
_____	_____

TOTAL [   ]

Please log your study hours with submission of your final exam. To log your study time, fill in the appropriate circle under question 25 of the FasTrax® answer sheet under the "Evaluation" section.

Nursing and Malpractice Risks: Understanding the Law

WESTERN SCHOOLS' NURSING
CONTINUING EDUCATION EVALUATION

Instructions: Mark your answers to the following questions with a black pen on the "Evaluation" section of your FasTrax® answer sheet provided with this course. You should not return this sheet. Please use the scale below to rate the following statements:

A Agree Strongly

B Agree Somewhat

C Disagree Somewhat

D Disagree Strongly

The course content met the following education objectives:

1. Discusses the various factors that determine the legal responsibilities of the practicing nurse.

2. Identifies the most common areas of liability for nurses.

3. Discusses the unique liability risks of nurses who practice in the emergency department, in obstetrics, in mental health, in the operating room, and in critical care.

4. Identifies how to ensure legal protection through correct documentation.

5. Discusses the legal implications of making work assignments, working in an understaffed situation, refusing a work assignment, floating, and mandatory overtime.

6. Discusses the basic rights that patients have and identifies situations that might jeopardize those rights.

7. Identifies the usual progression of a medical malpractice lawsuit, from the filing of the complaint through to the trial.

8. Identifies how personal liability insurance and the laws that offer protection from liability, protect the nurse.

9. The content of this course was relevant to the objectives.

10. This offering met my professional education needs.

11. The objectives met the overall purpose/goal of the course.

12. The course was generally well written and the subject matter explained thoroughly. (If no, please explain on the back of the FasTrax instruction sheet.)

13. The content of this course was appropriate for home study.

14. The final examination was well written and at an appropriate level for the content of the course.

Please complete the following research questions in order to help us better meet your educational needs. Pick the ONE answer which is most appropriate.

15. Which answer best describes the portion of your total Continuing Education hours that were completed by home study during your last renewal?
    A. All
    B. Half to more than half
    C. Less than half
    D. None

16. Are you reimbursed for your Continuing Education hours, and if so, by what dollar percentage?
    A. All
    B. Half to more than half
    C. Less than half
    D. None

17. What is your work status?
    A. Full-time employment
    B. Part-time employment
    C. Per diem/Temporary employment
    D. Inactive/Retired

18. For your LAST renewal did you take more Continuing Education contact hours than required by your state, if so, how many?
    A. 1–15 hours
    B. 16–30 hours
    C. 31 or more hours
    D. No, I only take the state required minimum

19. Do you usually exceed the contact hours required for your state license renewal, if so, why?
    A. Yes, I have more than one state license
    B. Yes, to meet additional special association Continuing Education requirements
    C. Yes, for professional self-interest/cross-training
    D. No, I only take the state required minimum

20. What nursing shift do you most commonly work?
    A. Morning Shift (Any shift starting after 3:00am or before 11:00am)
    B. Day/Afternoon Shift (Any shift starting after 11:00am or before 7:00pm)
    C. Night Shift (Any shift starting after 7:00pm or before 3:00am)
    D. I work rotating shifts

21. What was the SINGLE most important reason you chose this course?
    A. Low Price
    B. New or Newly revised course
    C. High interest/Required course topic
    D. Number of Contact Hours Needed

22. Where do you work? (If your place of employment is not listed below, please leave this question blank.)
    A. Hospital
    B. Medical Clinic/Group Practice/ HMO/Office setting
    C. Long Term Care/Rehabilitation Facility/Nursing Home
    D. Home Health Care Agency

23. Which field do you specialize in?
    A. Medical/Surgical
    B. Geriatrics
    C. Pediatrics/Neonatal
    D. Other

24. For your last renewal, how many months BEFORE your license expiration date did you order your course materials?
    A. 1–3 months
    B. 4–6 months
    C. 7–12 months
    D. Greater than 12 months

25. **PLEASE LOG YOUR STUDY HOURS WITH SUBMISSION OF YOUR FINAL EXAM.** Please choose which best represents the total study hours it took to complete this 30 hour course.
    A. less than 25 hours
    B. 25–28 hours
    C. 29–32 hours
    D. greater than 32 hours

CONTENTS

PRETEST

Begin by taking the pretest. Compare your answers on the pretest to the answer key (located in the back of the book). Circle those test items that you missed. The pretest answer key indicates the course chapters where the content of that question is discussed.

Next, read each chapter. Focus special attention on the chapters where you made incorrect answer choices. Study questions are provided at the end of each chapter so that you can assess your progress and understanding of the material.

1. The term malpractice is often used interchangeably with the legal term

    a. fiduciary duty.

    b. negligence.

    c. tortious conduct.

    d. invasion of privacy.

2. Criminal actions can be brought against nurses when they

    a. threaten a patient.

    b. breach the legal standard of care.

    c. intentionally injure patients or illegally obtain drugs.

    d. disrespect the attending physician.

3. The court may establish the standard of care applicable to a case by listening to

    a. testimony of expert witnesses.

    b. arguments by the plaintiff's attorney.

    c. arguments by the defendant's attorney.

    d. testimony of the plaintiff's spouse.

4. The expert witness serves to

    a. give advice on how to testify.

    b. evaluate how the jury is responding to testimony.

    c. evaluate the testimony of each witness.

    d. explain applicable standards of care.

5. Because of the risks associated with the inappropriate use of restraints inpatient, the new HCFA standards require that hospitals develop a least restrictive policy. This policy should focus on

    a. what is best for the nurse when staffing is short.

    b. what will most likely minimize the patient's mobility.

    c. function for the individual patient.

    d. the combined wishes of the family and the patient.

6. If a nurse notices a piece of equipment that needs repair, that nurse should

    a. fill out an incident report and pull the equipment from service.

    b. call the manufacturer and alert them to the problem.

    c. call the biomedical department and alert them to the problem.

    d. alert the nursing supervisor.

7. The Emergency Medical Treatment and Active Labor Act requires that

   a. all pregnant women be allowed to deliver their babies in any hospital they wish..

   b. all hospitals allow labor units to come in to speak with emergency department staff.

   c. a hospital provide an "appropriate medical screening" examination to any individual presenting to the emergency department requesting examination or treatment.

   d. hospitals screen only trauma patients and refer others to facilities less crowded.

8. When a doctor orders a patient transferred, who is held legally responsible for making sure the transfer occurs promptly?

   a. the doctor ordering the transfer

   b. the hospital transferring the patient

   c. the hospital receiving the patient

   d. the nurse caring for the patient

9. The area of health care where the most malpractice claims are filed is

   a. anesthesia.

   b. emergency department.

   c. radiology.

   d obstetrics.

10. Claims against long term care facilities tend to relate back to three key factors:

    a. leadership, staffing and documentation.

    b. patient falls, med errors and patient elopement.

    c. invasion of privacy, falls and staffing.

    d. medication errors, falls and burns.

11. On which part of the medical record may nonlicensed personnel chart?

    a. progress notes only

    b. nursing notes, if the charge nurse has so authorized

    c. flow sheets and checklists

    d. on no part of the record

12. If a doctor orders something with which a nurse disagrees, but which the nurse does not feel could be life-threatening, that nurse should

    a. complete the order as requested.

    b. voice concern, but then complete the order as requested if the doctor insists and document the situation.

    c. notify the supervisor.

    d. refuse to complete the order.

13. A nursing care plan should

    a. be written in pencil to allow for easy changes.

    b. be maintained as a part of the medical record.

    c. discarded when the patient is discharged.

    d. sent home with the patient at discharge.

14. A claim of contributory negligence would have no effect if the patient

    a. were postoperative.

    b. were confused or disoriented.

    c. had a terminal illness.

    d. disagreed with the doctor's instructions.

15. If another nurse does not arrive to take over patient care, what are the nurse's legal responsibilities?

    a. The nurse is responsible for completing the eight-hour shift, and then is free to leave.

    b. The nurse has an obligation to deliver reasonable or minimal assistance.

    c. The nurse is bound to stay and care for the patient for another eight hours.

    d. the nurse is obligated to find a qualified nurse to assume care.

16. The Health Insurance Portability and Accountability Act (HIPAA) released in the Fall of 2000 defines a patient's rights in the areas of

    a. privacy, confidentiality of medical records and access to medical records.

    b. security, privacy and medical information.

    c. access to care, rights to experimental care and privacy.

    d. provider accountability, insurance portability and medical record privacy.

17. In which instance would the court most likely override a patient's wish to refuse treatment?

    a. if the patient were pregnant, and her refusal of treatment could harm her unborn child

    b. if the patient is terminal

    c. if the lack of treatment will cause the patient's condition to worsen

    d. if treatment could help the patient's condition, although side affects would occur

18. One reason not to depend on an employer's insurance is

    a. most hospitals will not cover their employees.

    b. most hospitals cover their employees as "additional insureds."

    c. the insurance will not pay if a nurse has been negligent.

    d. courts may bar coverage by an employer's policy.

19. Under what circumstances can an occurrence policy present a coverage dilemma?

    a. if more than one claim results in the same year

    b. if the patient delays making a claim

    c. if the exact date of the incident is unclear

    d. if the patient has died

20. In what situation would the Good Samaritan Law not offer you protection?

    a. if you know the victim

    b. if you accept money for your services

    c. if you don't have your nursing license with you

    d. if the victim is taken to a hospital other than the one where you work

INTRODUCTION

As a nurse, your risk of being named in a medical malpractice case is greater than ever before. As nurses continue to expand their roles and achieve professional recognition, they will be held to an ever higher level of accountability, and their risk of being sued will be even greater.

At one time, nurses were not individually named in medical malpractice lawsuits because they were not regarded as professionals responsible for their own actions. Today, however, that has changed. The public recognizes that nurses have certain skills and are able to function independently. Along with that recognition, nurses must accept the fact that they will be held accountable for their actions. Nurses must keep in mind, also, that being unaware of the laws governing their practice is not a valid defense in any type of lawsuit. As practicing professionals, it is the nurses responsibility to know the laws governing their practice and to ensure that their care is up to professional standards.

As managed care becomes the dominant health care delivery model, many opportunities emerge for nursing. These opportunities can create new areas of liability for nurses, particularly as they assume expanded roles and work outside the traditional hospital setting. In addition, the increased use of clinical pathways or other treatment guidelines, which are more frequently being utilized to control resources in the care of particular patients, can create liability if not correctly understood and used. Nurses working as case managers or utilization managers who are employed by managed care organizations may also find that they are subject to new and increasing liabilities. Understanding the liability associated with utilization management and learning how to minimize it will be an important part of the utilization managers' job.

You will note as you read through this course that many new sections have been included that describe potential new liability risks for nurses created by the managed care delivery model as they relate to each of the sections contained in the course. The goal of this book is to familiarize you with some of your legal responsibilities as a nurse and to teach you how to protect yourself legally while rendering the best care possible. Recognize that many of the issues such as documentation, falls prevention, medication administration and staffing present the nurse with the same potential for liability regardless of the setting in which the nurse might practice. However, this book is not meant to give professional legal advice. It is, rather, a guide meant to give you a broad overview of some of the legal factors affecting the practice of nursing today. If you have specific questions, or if you are having legal difficulties, you should seek the services of a practicing health care attorney.

CHAPTER 1

MEDICAL MALPRACTICE: HOW GREAT IS THE RISK?

CHAPTER OBJECTIVE

After studying this chapter, the reader will be able to identify the legal responsibilities of the practicing nurse.

LEARNING OBJECTIVES

After reading this chapter, the reader will be able to

1. define and clarify the difference between negligence and malpractice.

2. identify at least three sources for the laws that regulate the practice of nursing.

3. define the meaning of standard of care and explain its role in medical malpractice lawsuits.

4. identify the four elements of negligence used to substantiate a claim of medical malpractice.

5. define the doctrine of res ipsa loquitur and describe the instances in which it would be applied.

6. discuss two theories of shared liability.

7. discuss the special legal risks of agency nurses, independent contractors, student nurses, nursing administrators and advanced nurse practitioners.

THE MEANING OF MALPRACTICE

The terms negligence and malpractice are often used interchangeably. Malpractice, however, is actually a specific type of negligence. Negligence occurs when someone fails to do something that a reasonably prudent person would do in a similar situation, or when someone does something that a reasonably prudent person would not do. Malpractice is a specific type of negligence and is usually applied to professionals. Malpractice occurs when a professional fails to follow a standard of care prevalent for the profession and thereby harms another person. This can cover a large number of areas. For nurses, malpractice ranges from being negligent when caring for a patient to betraying a patient's confidence. Criminal actions can also be brought against nurses when they intentionally injure patients or illegally obtain drugs, but this occurs less frequently.

State v. King, Golz, Fitchette: Medication Error or Manslaughter?

There has been a recent proclivity of filing criminal actions in health care and it is not just directed at physicians, it has also been directed at nurses. As an example, in 1997, criminal indictments were filed in Denver (and reported in the *Denver Post* on April 29, 1997) against three nurses for administering the wrong dosage of a medication as well as via the wrong route. They were charged with involuntary manslaughter.

The case involved a healthy baby boy born at a Denver Hospital to a mother who had a previous history of syphilis. The physician wrote an order for an intramuscular (IM) injection of penicillin G as a precaution. The pharmacist misread the dosage and filled the syringes with a dose in excess of what was ordered, but did label the medication as IM only. Nurse King, the primary nurse, was concerned that the IM route of administration would mean that the infant would have to be stuck repeatedly. King consulted with two nursing supervisors, Nurse Golz and Nurse Fitchette. Golz, a pediatric nurse practitioner, changed the route of administration from intramuscular to intravenous (IV) without consulting with the pharmacist or the physician. The infant suffered a cardiac arrest within three hours of the IV injection.

An investigation following the death of the child led the Colorado Board of Nursing to suspend the licenses of the two supervisors for a year, followed by a two-year probation. The primary nurse, King, was not disciplined by the board. The Adams County District Attorney determined that the conduct of all three nurses constituted "gross negligence." He pursued a felony charge of criminal negligent homicide, which is defined by Colorado law as a gross deviation from the standard of care that causes the death of another person. A guilty verdict would require a jail term of one to three years and a fine of up to one million dollars.

Golz and Fitchette plead guilty to the charge of criminal negligent homicide. The judge in the case ordered a deferred judgement of two years. One of the conditions of the deferment required a public service component which included the education of nursing students regarding the facts of the case. After two years the nurses would be able to withdraw their guilty pleas and the case against them would be dismissed. King, the primary nurse, chose to go to trial and was found not guilty of criminal negligent homicide. Although this course is not designed to provide detailed information related to criminal law and its impact on nurses, it is important to understand the difference between criminal law and malpractice. In criminal law the state files charges against the nurse alleging an intentional violation of a law written to protect the public from harm. If found guilty, the nurse can be imprisoned and loss of license is also likely to occur.

When considering a charge of malpractice, the courts do not take into account the professional's motives or attitude. This means that you can have the best of motives, and be totally committed to your patients, and yet, if you deviate from the standards of care established for the nursing profession, you may be found negligent and forced to pay money damages.

On the other hand, while your attitude may not influence the court once a malpractice claim is made, it could very well influence whether a suit is filed in the first place. Granted, lawsuits are often filed when patients are not satisfied with the outcome of their care. However, during the initial interview with an attorney most patients complain about the attitudes of the health care providers, not about the technical aspects of their care. A patient may be angry feeling the nurse did not explain things properly, disregarded privacy or was rude. Of course, a nurse is not guilty of malpractice because of rudeness to a patient. However, a good attorney, upon reviewing the patient's medical record, may find several deviations from the standards of care on which to base a lawsuit. This includes things that you may have overlooked, such as an improperly performed procedure or omitted treatments. Then, once the case reaches trial, the attorney can use the allegation that the nurse was rude or uncaring to engender the jury's sympathy for the patient.

You need to recognize that, although the laws relating to nursing are fairly clear, juries who decide cases are most often lay people. For any number of reasons, including emotional factors, juries may decide a case in favor of the plaintiff regardless of the facts of the case or the relevant law. The safest course is to always treat patients fairly and with compassion; remember that a patient who feels that doctors and nurses have done their best is not as likely to sue as a patient who feels ignored or neglected.

Criminal Charges Brought Against Nurses

In 1997 criminal charges were brought against nurses for administering the wrong dosage of a medication as well as for administering the dosage via the wrong route. They were charged with involuntary manslaughter.

SOURCES OF NURSING LAW

The laws that govern the practice of nursing come from a variety of sources. This means that there is no one document that spells out your legal rights and responsibilities as a professional nurse. And, perhaps to confuse things further, the laws change, reflecting the changing role of the nurse. To begin to understand your legal responsibilities as a nurse, it is important that you know where the laws that affect your practice originate.

The first source of laws affecting nursing is the United States Constitution. You are probably familiar with the basic premise of the Constitution, which is to ensure each individual's rights to life, liberty, and religious freedom. The Constitution also affects the practice of nursing in that it guides the courts in deciding the patient's right to life, right to die, and right to refuse treatment.

A second source of laws are legislatures, both state and federal. The laws written by legislatures are called statutes, which become effective after being signed by the governor, in the case of state statutes, or by the president, in the case of federal statutes. Of particular interest to nurses is a series of state statutes called the nurse practice acts. Nurse practice acts define the legal limits for the practice of nursing; specify the conditions for licensure for RNs, LPNs, and special areas of nursing practice; and list violations that can result in disciplinary action. Nurse practice acts also establish a state board of nursing to make sure that the provisions specified in the act are enforced. The state board's duties include establishing and certifying curriculums for nursing education programs, establishing criteria for obtaining licensure, and conducting investigations and hearings regarding violations of the nurse practice act. These acts specify the number of people who should serve on the board and what their educational and professional backgrounds should be. Furthermore, the board can effectively carry out the objectives of the nurse practice act because it has the authority to enact rules or regulations. These rules and regulations are still another source of law that affects the practice of nursing.

But perhaps of greatest interest to nurses is the area of law called common law. Based on the decisions of the courts, common law deals with most of the issues of malpractice. Common law is formed when, through the process of settling a dispute, a court renders a decision. When making its decision, the court interprets relevant statutes and may also consider the intent of the legislators who enacted the statutes. The resultant decision establishes a precedent, which may influence the outcome of future cases involving similar issues.

Unfortunately, though, not all of the decisions of the courts are available for review. For example, cases that are settled either before or during trial—which occurs in the majority of all medical malpractice cases—are not published. When a malpractice case does go to trial, it is first heard in what is called trial court. The results of trial cases are usually published only in the county in which they are heard and, therefore, are not available for wide review. If one of the parties in the case is dissatisfied with the decision of the trial court, the party can appeal and have the case heard in appellate court and in some cases the state and the United States Supreme Court. To appeal, one must question a point of law decided by the trial court. Once the appellate court or Supreme Court has reached a decision in the case, that decision is published, making it available for review. However, the published decision may focus more on the point of law in dispute rather than the details of the alleged malpractice.

Nevertheless, numerous cases are available for study that involve similar circumstances, such as falls or medication errors. By studying the court's decisions in these cases, you will have a good idea how the court views your responsibilities as a professional nurse. It is important to understand, though, that the decisions on cases tried in your own state will take precedence over decisions of courts in other states.

HOW THE NURSE PRACTICE ACT AFFECTS YOU

The content of nurse practice acts vary from state to state, but, regardless of the state, the wording of these statutes tends to be broad. The act in your state will give you general guidelines to help you stay within the legal limits of nursing practice, but it will not tell you how to perform specific procedures or carry out your everyday functions. For that type of information, you should consult your hospital's policies and procedures manual. There you will find details regarding the extent of your responsibilities within that par-

ticular hospital. Realize that a hospital may restrict you to an even narrower scope of responsibility than that allowed by the nurse practice act; however, it cannot authorize you to take on responsibilities that the act prohibits. Recognize also the importance of keeping policies and procedures current and reflective of nursing practice within your hospital. Often, the hospital's policy and procedure manual is the only evidence available to prove that you provided the appropriate standard of care.

STANDARDS OF NURSING CARE

The basis of every medical malpractice lawsuit involving a nurse is the claim that the nurse failed to maintain a certain standard of care while caring for the patient. This standard of care is the level of care a reasonably prudent nurse—in other words, a nurse with average intelligence and like training and experience—would have rendered in the same or similar circumstances. Although the courts occasionally consider the standard of care to differ depending upon the location where the care was rendered, most states now believe that a minimum standard of care exists for every state in the country. Therefore, whether you practice nursing in New York or Wyoming, the care you give your patients is expected to meet the same standard. And any time your care falls below this standard, you risk malpractice liability.

The standards of care change with each medical advance that affects patient care, and you're responsible for keeping abreast of those changes. This means that you must continually update your skills and expand your knowledge. Some of the ways you can gain knowledge is through reading nursing journals and attending inservice programs and conferences. After all, you will be held accountable for the standards that exist at the time you render your care—not the standards that you learned in nursing school, which may have been years earlier. Claiming ignorance of a new procedure or technique is no defense in a medical malpractice lawsuit.

In addition, over the past few years there has been considerable attention paid to the development and use of clinical pathways or practice guidelines to standardize the care provided to patients with the same clinical condition or diagnosis. Nurses are often involved in both the development and utilization of these tools and need to be aware of the benefits and the potential liabilities that they may create. During the development of guidelines or pathways, nurses should recognize the importance that these tools reflect prevailing standards in order to ensure their validity. Nurses should treat each patient as an individual by realizing that not all patients are appropriate candidates for the use of these guidelines or pathways.

In 1973, the American Nurses' Association (ANA) compiled a set of general standards for nursing practice that they felt should be applied to nurses in all settings. From there, specialty divisions of the ANA—such as Community Health, Maternal-Child, and Mental Health—established more detailed standards pertinent to those specialty areas. The standards specify the minimum level of conduct by which a nurse in that area should be held accountable. Be aware that if you ever accept an assignment in a specialty area, you will be held accountable to the minimum standards of care for that specialty, even if you normally practice in another area. As nursing practice changes and more nurses engage in independent practice, expect the standards to also evolve. To be safe always check with the state(s) nursing board which governs your practice.

During a medical malpractice trial, the patient (called the plaintiff) will try to show that the nurse (called the defendant) failed to maintain an appropriate standard of care. To do this, the plaintiff will first try to prove what standards were appropriate at the time care was received. This may be done in a variety of ways.

First, the general standards compiled by the ANA or those established by one of its specialty divisions may be introduced into evidence. The nurse practice act, guidelines written by the Joint Commission on Accreditation of Healthcare Organizations (JCAHO), state regulations (such as from the Department of Health), or guidelines in nursing textbooks may be submitted to further prove what the appropriate standard of care was when care was received.

Other sources of established standards of care are a hospital's policies and procedures, which are usually much more specific regarding a nurse's responsibilities. It is important that you realize that some policy and procedure manuals may actually establish a higher standard of care than that generally accepted as the minimum standard. If so, it is to this higher standard that you will be held accountable. It is also important to recognize the importance of keeping hospital policies and procedures current ensuring that they are truly reflective of nursing practice within the organization. Out-of-date policies can prevent an attorney from being able to adequately defend a nurse accused of negligence.

The plaintiff may ask an expert on the topic in question to explain the appropriate standards of care to the court. This expert is usually a nurse who is proficient in the same area as the nurse who has been charged with malpractice. Non-nursing professionals, such as doctors, have also been used in some cases, although this may not be allowed in all states. After describing the standard of care, the expert witness then compares the care the defendant gave with those standards.

Another example of something that the plaintiff may use to evaluate whether a nurse failed to maintain the appropriate standard of care is the nursing care plan. For example, if the nursing care plan specified that the side rails on the patient's bed were to be elevated at all times, and the patient fell out of bed because the side rails were lowered, then this would be evidence that the nurse did not meet the agreed-upon standard of care. But, if the patient had been constantly trying to get up unassisted, and if the nursing care plan reflected that fact along with various attempts to control the problem, then the care plan could be used to defend the nurse. For this reason, it is important always to maintain nursing care plans as a part of the permanent medical record.

But the courts are not limited to only one source to decide the appropriate standard of care. For example, in *Pisel v. Stamford Community Hospital* (1980), the court used expert witness testimony, ANA standards, and federal regulations to establish the standard of care. In this suit, an unsupervised patient in a mental health hospital wedged her head between the bed frame and the side rail, causing permanent neurologic damage. The patient's family sued both the nurses and the hospital for malpractice. The court found both the hospital and the nurses guilty of malpractice based on certain key facts. First, the nurses should not have left the patient in a steel bed while in a seclusion room. Second, the nurses did not constantly observe the patient, and then, even though the patient's behavior was acutely psychotic, they did not notify the patient's doctor. They also failed to follow written medical orders. Adding fuel to the fire was the fact that the nurses destroyed their original notes and wrote new ones after the incident occurred. This helped to support the belief that they knew of their negligence.

Despite all of the written standards regarding nurses, the courts may even judge a nurse's behavior by standards of care not usually considered to be nursing standards. For example, in 1987, the family of a 66-year-old man sued a Louisiana hospital, claiming that a graduate nurse failed to diagnose his myocardial infarction *(Story v. St. Mary Parish Service District)*. In this instance, the man had a history of high blood pressure and had been taking hydrochlorothiazide for hypertension for five years. Although the man had been admitted to the hospital for gastrointestinal complaints, he began complaining to nurses two days after his admission of shortness of breath and severe elbow and chest pain. The graduate nurse noted in the chart that the man complained of elbow pain and further stated that the man admitted that he had arthritis. She also noted that he appeared slightly short of breath. The graduate nurse then wrote that she would have the patient medicated for pain, which he was, twenty minutes later. Forty minutes after that, the man died due to a myocardial infarction.

Although diagnosis is generally accepted to be an area of physician responsibility, the plaintiff's attorney argued in the lawsuit that the graduate nurse failed to appreciate the patient's complaints and interpret the findings. The key here was that at no time did the graduate nurse note that she consulted the charge nurse about the patient's complaints nor did she attempt to contact the patient's doctor. The graduate nurse failed to maintain a proper standard of care by failing to understand that the patient's complaints were of a serious nature. The family settled the suit out of court for $200,000.

The courts may also decide to use only ordinary common sense when establishing the appropriate standard of care. For example, in *Jones v. Hawkes Hospital* (1964), a nurse was sued for malpractice after leaving a sedated patient, who was in labor, to assist a doctor with another patient. While the nurse was out of the room, the patient got out of bed, fell, and seriously injured herself. The nurse explained to the court that the hospital had a policy that stated that a nurse had to be present when a doctor attended a patient in labor; therefore, she had felt compelled to leave the patient to help the doctor with the other patient. The nurse asked the court to allow an expert witness to testify to establish the standard of care. The court denied the request, stating that any reasonably prudent person could decide the outcome of the case based solely on ordinary experience and knowledge. And, using common sense as a guide, the jury found the nurse negligent.

PROVING A CLAIM OF MALPRACTICE

Establishing a standard of care is only one aspect of a malpractice case. The plaintiff must prove several factors to substantiate such a claim.

Duty

First, the plaintiff must prove that the patient and the nurse had established a legal nurse-patient relationship that required the nurse to deliver the appropriate standard of care. This is what is known as duty. Duty usually occurs when you're assigned to a specific patient, but it can also occur if you see that an unassigned patient needs some type of help. In that instance, you have a duty to help the patient yourself or to see that they get the help which is needed. If you work in a clinic setting, duty may occur through a simple telephone call when the patient asks for advice. You also have a duty to a patient, whether assigned to your care or not, if you see the patient receiving inferior care from either a doctor or another nurse. Rather than observing passively, the law expects you to intervene on the patient's behalf. However, you do not have a duty to render nursing care to everyone. For example, if you see someone injured in a car accident, the law does not require you to intervene. If you do decide to help, though, you must give care that meets the professional standard. Most courts agree that when a patient presents for care and care commences, a legal and contractual duty is established.

Breach of Duty

Once the plaintiff establishes that the nurse had a duty to deliver nursing care, they must then prove that the nurse breached that duty. In other words, the plaintiff must prove that the nurse's care fell below the acceptable standard of care and, thus, that the nurse was negligent. But the case does not end there. The plaintiff must then prove that an injury resulted as a direct result of the nurse's negligence. This is known as causation.

Causation

Causation—also called proximate cause—is more difficult to prove than either duty or breach of duty. This is because, even though the patient may have an obvious injury, the cause of the injury may not be clear. Also, it may be possible to suggest other causes for the injury, only one of which may have been the nurse's negligence. A good example of this is when a patient develops an infection following surgery. Although the patient may believe that a negligent act caused the infection, it could be difficult to prove. Was the doctor responsible? Was the nurse? Did the infection result from improper handwashing or improperly sterilized instruments, or did it occur because infections occur in a certain number of cases despite the best techniques? The plaintiff usually tries to establish proximate cause through the testimony of an expert witness. The expert witness attempts to explain that, if it had not been for the conduct of the defendant, the patient would not have been injured. This does not mean that more than one person cannot be responsible for the patient's injury. It just means that—if a nurse is named in a lawsuit—that nurse's actions would have to have contributed substantially to the patient's injury.

In some cases, causation may be so clear that an expert witness is not necessary. Just such a case was *Carter v. Anderson Memorial Hospital* (1985), which involved a patient who had just had abdominal surgery. Two student nurses were bringing a portable x-ray machine into the patient's room when the wheels became caught in some electrical cords. The machine fell on the patient and injured his arm and abdomen. In this case, it is obvious that if the x-ray machine had not fallen on the patient, he would not have been injured.

Foreseeability

Another issue courts consider when evaluating both breach of duty and causation is foreseeability. Foreseeability is the concept that a health care provider has a responsibility to foresee harm and eliminate risks. For example, if you work in the operating room and you leave the room without advising another nurse about their responsibility for the sponge count, then you would have failed in your duty. The same thing goes for letting a patient with known suicidal tendencies leave the unit and wander about unattended. In this instance, you should be able to foresee that the patient could be harmed while unattended. In *Stevenson v. Alta Bates* (1937), two nurses were helping a patient who had had a stroke walk to the hospital sunroom. When they reached the sunroom, one nurse released her grip on the patient and stepped forward to ready a chair for the patient. But, after the nurse removed the support of her hand, the patient fell and broke her hip. The court ruled that the patient was entitled to compensation because the nurse should have been able to foresee the patient's need for a chair before bringing the patient to the sunroom.

An example of a case where the plaintiff failed to prove foreseeability is *Hodge v. Crafts-Farrow State Hospital* (1985). This case involved a woman who was admitted to the hospital for a CT scan to rule out a possible head injury. The patient received 5 mg. of Valium for sedation, after which she developed respiratory distress. She subsequently contracted pneumonia and died 10 days later. In this instance, the court ruled that no evidence existed that showed that the hospital staff should have been able to foresee that the patient would have an adverse reaction to the Valium that would lead to her death.

Res Ipsa Loquitur

Because causation is so difficult to prove, the courts occasionally allow plaintiffs to argue their case using the theory of res ipsa loquitur. The literal translation of the phrase means "the thing speaks for itself." What it refers to is a situation in which negligence is presumed because no other explanation for the patient's injury exists. Three conditions must be satisfied before the court will allow the use of res ipsa loquitur. These are (1) the injury must be of a type that would not ordinarily occur unless someone were negligent, (2) the defendant must have had exclusive control over whatever caused the plaintiff's injury, and (3) the injury could not have resulted from anything the plaintiff voluntarily did.

When the doctrine of res ipsa loquitur is used, the plaintiff is allowed to prove negligence by presenting only circumstantial evidence. This is opposite from most malpractice cases; ordinarily, the court presumes that the defendant used ordinary care until the plaintiff proves otherwise.

The first malpractice case to ever use res ipsa loquitur was *Ybarra v. Spangard* in 1944. In this case, the plaintiff was admitted to the hospital for an appendectomy. After he awakened from the anesthesia, he had severe pain in his right shoulder. The pain continued to intensify even after his discharge from the hospital. Eventually, the muscles in the patient's shoulder atrophied and became paralyzed. The plaintiff—who stated that he had never had pain in his shoulder before the appendectomy—sued everyone involved: his attending physician, the surgeon, the nurses, the anesthetist, and the owner of the hospital.

Although the plaintiff could not prove who caused his injury, it was obvious that the injury had occurred in the operating room. Because shoulder pain should not result from an appendectomy, it was obvious that someone had been negligent. That satisfied the first rule of res ipsa loquitur. The second rule was satisfied because the defendants had exclusive control over the operating room. And the third rule was satisfied because the patient was under the effects of anesthesia and could not have voluntarily contributed to his injury. As a result, the court allowed the plaintiff to apply the doctrine of res ipsa loquitur, and all of the defendants were found equally liable.

In another recent case, *Fieux v. Cardiovascular & Thoracic Clinic* (1999), the operating room team left a clamp behind the patient's heart following open heart surgery. A routine chest x-ray after the surgery revealed the clamp. The patient was forced to undergo a second surgical procedure within a few hours of the first to remove the clamp. The court held that a failure of the operating room staff to perform an instrument count was sufficient to establish negligence without the use of expert testimony.

Damages

The final aspect of the plaintiff's case involves the matter of damages. This means that the plaintiff must show that he suffered some type of damage because of his injury, and that he is entitled to monetary compensation because of that damage. Damages may be general, special, or punitive. General damages include compensation for any disfigurement or disability as well as for past, present, and future pain and suffering. Special damages include compensation for all of the plaintiff's medical expenses as well as for income he lost, or may lose in the future, because of his injury. The court may award punitive damages to punish the defendant if the court feels that the defendant was grossly or intentionally negligent. Occasionally, the plaintiff may seek compensation for emotional damages, which includes anxiety or emotional distress associated with an injury. Some states, how-

ever, limit the amount of damages a plaintiff can recover, especially those relating to pain and suffering and punitive damages.

YOUR EMPLOYER'S RESPONSIBILITY FOR YOUR PERFORMANCE

Even if you are one day named in a lawsuit accusing you of malpractice, you probably will not be the only defendant. The hospital or other organization where you work will no doubt also be held responsible for your actions. In legal terms, this expanded liability is called respondeat superior, or vicarious liability. The reasoning behind respondeat superior is that an employer hires its own employees, trains its own employees, and controls the conduct of its employees. Therefore, the law feels that an employer should have some responsibility for the actions of its employees. If nothing else, the law hopes to encourage employers to choose its employees carefully and then to diligently supervise those employees. In addition, the courts recognize that an employer is usually in a better position to pay any damages awarded to a plaintiff than is the offending employee.

The doctrine of respondeat superior protects you somewhat because, as long as you are acting under your employer's direction, you will not have to bear the brunt of a malpractice claim alone. Keep in mind, though, that this doctrine does not relieve you of the responsibility for your own actions, especially when you clearly violate hospital policy. Instead of shifting any blame away from you, it simply expands the blame to your employer.

An example of respondeat superior doctrine in action is the case of *Variety Children's Hospital v. Perkins* (1980), where the hospital was held liable for the acts of its nurses and residents. In this case, a child had undergone a tracheotomy procedure.

Postoperatively the patient did well and was transferred up to the intensive care unit. Later, the patient ceased breathing. Before the child could be successfully resuscitated, the child sustained severe irreversible brain damage. The cause of the respiratory difficulty was attributed to the build up of subcutaneous emphysema (air under the skin tissues), which caused the child's lung to collapse. The court found that the nurses and the residents were negligent in not observing the symptoms of subcutaneous emphysema, which by the evidence at trial appeared to be present for almost two hours before the patient stopped breathing. The nurse and the resident were employees of the hospital as they provided services to the patients that were billed by the hospital. According to the doctrine of respondeat superior, as employees, the hospital was liable for the negligence of the nurses and residents involved.

THE BORROWED SERVANT DOCTRINE

An extension of the practice of shared liability is the borrowed servant doctrine. This occurs when the hospital, as the employer, lends the services of one of its nurses to a third party. A key example is when a hospital staff nurse assists a surgeon in the operating room. Surgeons generally are not hospital employees. Therefore, if the surgeon controls the actions of the nurse assisting in surgery, then it is the surgeon who is responsible if those actions are negligent.

This issue becomes less than clear when you consider that the hospital may have been responsible for training the nurse and may have, in effect, certified to the surgeon that the nurse was qualified to act as an assistant. For this reason, shared liability where everyone involved shares part of the blame occurs much more often than does the borrowed servant doctrine.

In *Brown v. Starmed Staffing* (1997), the hospital admitted the patient into the Emergency Room ("ER") because he was having difficulty swallowing and his tongue was swollen. The patient's doctor made the determination that the symptoms were due to an allergic reaction to blood pressure medication. At the request of the physician, the patient's wife brought all of the patient's medications to the hospital. On the direction of the doctor's verbal order, the ER nurse administered the patient's regular dose of the blood pressure medication suspected of causing the allergic reaction. The physician discharged the patient later that day. After discharge, the patient suffered another allergic reaction and choked to death.

At trial, the plaintiff alleged that the company which provided nursing staff for the hospital was liable for the nurse's action. The plaintiff argued that the company paid the nurse's wages, provided health insurance, worker's compensations, and required the nurse to abide by the company's rules. However, the court held that it was the hospital that had control over the nurse's conduct when he administered the medication. Therefore, the nurse was a borrowed servant. The court did find that the hospital was liable under respondeat superior.

THE LEGAL RISKS OF SPECIAL NURSING GROUPS

The principle of shared liability exists for almost all nurses. However, the type and extent of your employer's liability may vary, depending on your position and your employer.

Agency Nurses

The legal role of the agency nurse is still evolving. In general, though, if you work for an agency, you have an employer-employee relationship with that agency. This means that the agency may be vicariously liable for your actions under the doctrine of respondeat superior. However, the courts have occasionally steered away from this interpretation when the agency nurse performs staff relief work in a hospital.

In this instance, although you are still employed by the agency, the agency has temporarily "lent" your services to the hospital. Therefore, since the hospital is your temporary "employer," it could then be held liable for your actions under the borrowed servant doctrine. If you work for an agency, be sure to check with that agency to determine who, under the terms of your contract, would assume liability in a case of malpractice.

Regardless of who else may be liable, you need to be especially cautious if you perform hospital staff relief work for an agency. The first step in protecting yourself is to make absolutely certain that you understand—and follow—the policies and procedures of every hospital that you work for. If you do not understand how the hospital handles a certain procedure, ask the head nurse or supervisor. Proceeding to perform a task in a manner that is different from that hospital's protocol could place you at risk.

You also need to make certain that you perform only duties that a particular hospital authorizes its nurses to perform. If you take on more responsibilities than you should, and then commit a negligent act, you could be responsible for paying all damages yourself, depending on the terms of your contract with your agency.

This same advice applies to working in a patient's home. There, you will need to follow your agency's policies and procedures to the letter. Also, do not ever perform non-nursing functions for the patient, and do not change the patient's nursing regimen unless your agency has instructed you to do so. If you do, and you are later named in a lawsuit, you may be the only one liable for your actions.

If you are a hospital staff nurse working with an agency nurse, your legal responsibilities are the same as when you work with any other member of the health care team. That is, if you see that the agency nurse is incompetent and believe that the patient may be at risk, you have a duty to intervene on the patient's behalf. This includes keeping the nurse from providing care to the patient and notifying your nursing supervisor.

Independent Contractors

If you perform private duty nursing, but you work for yourself instead of through an agency, then you are what is known as an independent contractor. Independent contractors are hired for a specific period of time and for a specific task. In this instance, an employer would not control your actions; you would perform your duties according to your own discretion. For this reason, the theory of respondeat superior would not apply and you would be solely liable for your actions.

Hospitals and other employers aren't free from all liability, however. They are responsible for hiring competent independent contractors. Therefore, they could be held liable for the actions of an independent contractor if they did not gather appropriate information about your competence, and you then negligently injured a third party. For this reason, you can expect a hospital to scrutinize your credentials before allowing you to care for a patient in a particular institution.

If you work in a hospital as a private duty nurse, you would be right to expect the hospital to provide you with all necessary equipment and support. If you work in the patient's home, though, you would be responsible for obtaining and correctly using any equipment the patient needs. And this naturally increases your risk for making a mistake. Regardless of the setting, remember that you will be held accountable to the same standard of care as is any other nurse in your state.

If you are a staff nurse, and a private duty nurse is caring for one of the patients on your unit, you are not totally free from all of your responsibility. As a member of the hospital staff, you are also responsible for that patient. You should again observe for any sign that the private duty nurse is performing negligently. And, if so, and that the patient may be harmed, then you must intervene, whether by telling your charge nurse or by directly stopping the nurse's actions.

Student Nurses

You may be surprised to learn that student nurses run the same risk for liability as do graduate professional nurses. Whenever student nurses work in a particular area, they are held accountable to the same standards of care as any other nurse practicing in that area. After all, the patient has a right to expect quality care, regardless of who is delivering it.

While the student nurse may be held accountable to the same standards of care, liability for an act of malpractice by a student nurse may extend to the student's instructor or to a nurse preceptor. When you work with student nurses, your main responsibility is to make assignments based on the students' experiences and competence. Then, you need to be available to supervise the students, if necessary. If the student's instructor makes the assignments, then the instructor is responsible for assessing the student's competence and for supervising the student.

Be assured that you are not automatically liable for the acts of a student nurse. Students have a responsibility not to attempt assignments for which they are not qualified, and not to perform tasks that they were not assigned. If a student has been assigned to a patient who requires more care than they are capable of delivering, then that student is responsible for letting you know.

Nurse Administrators

Nurse administrators may also be held liable for the actions of the nurses they direct. To begin with, nurse administrators have a responsibility to hire and maintain a competent staff. This involves checking a prospective nurse's credentials and licensure before hiring, and regularly evaluating that nurse's competence after they are hired. To make sure the nurse remains competent, the administrator must provide educational opportunities, such as arranging in-house inservices, allowing attendance to continuing education programs, and providing current reference material.

Other responsibilities of nurse administrators include development of up-to-date policies and procedures, assurance of nursing compliance with those policies and procedures, and establishment of an effective quality assurance program. Finally, nurse administrators are responsible for making sure that the staff nurses have the equipment they need and the appropriate number of staff to render safe care.

Licensed Practical Nurses

Licensed practical nurses and licensed vocational nurses are held accountable to a standard of care similar to that of the registered nurse. Of course, the duties of the LPN are more restricted than those of the RN. As LPNs fulfill ever expanding roles, they need to make sure that they are not taking on responsibilities that the law prohibits. If your hospital has trained you to perform certain tasks that ordinarily would not be your responsibility—such as administering medications—and the law in your state does not forbid this, then you are probably safe. However, even though you have been trained, you still need to make sure that your hospital has a written policy regarding the role of the LPN in administering drugs. If the policy is not written, you would have a hard time backing up your actions in court.

Above all it is important for both LPNs and RNs to realize that there are certain duties that LPNs are not allowed to perform. Even in the most short-staffed situations, an LPN should not perform any task which the organization has not authorized. A good example is *Flushing Hospital & Medical Center v. Local 1199* (1988). This case involved a nurse attendant, but it easily could have been an LPN.

In this situation, a patient called the nurse attendant because his I.V. bag was empty. The patient was afraid that air would enter his vein. The nurse attendant searched, without success, for an RN for about 15 minutes by using the intercom and by looking in most of the rooms. At this point, the nurse attendant felt that something had to be done. She had been shown how to change an I.V. bag by an RN in the past, and she had, in fact, hung I.V. bags during emergencies. Therefore, the nurse attendant took it upon herself to change the I.V. bag. As soon as she located an RN, the nurse attendant told her what she had done. The RN checked the bag and found everything in order. However, the patient later complained, and the incident came to the attention of the Assistant Director of Nursing. As a result, the nurse attendant was fired. After a legal battle, and a strong reprimand from the court, the nurse attendant was reinstated.

Besides the fact that you would not want to have to endure that kind of a fight, consider also the possible legal ramifications. If the nurse attendant had made some type of a mistake when hanging the bag, and the patient had been injured, then she could have been found guilty of malpractice. And, since she was assuming duties that were not in her job description, she could have been solely responsible for any damages. The most important thing to remember is to be certain of what duties the hospital allows you to perform and then perform only those duties.

Advanced Nurse Practitioner

There have been many attempts to set higher standards of practice for advanced nurse practitioners. Recently, the National Council of State Boards of Nursing (NCSBN) proposed requiring a second license for advanced practice nurses to representatives of advanced nurse practice organizations and certification boards. These nurses would include nurse practitioners, clinical nurse specialists, nurse midwives, and nurse anesthetists. This represents a dramatic change for NCSBN's earlier position.

Under the auspices of protecting the public safety and welfare, the NCSBN is now proposing immediate and mandatory licensure of all advanced practice nurses. Such licensure, entitled "Advanced Practice Registered Nurse" (APRN), will encompass all nurses who are nurse practitioners, clinical nurse specialists, nurse midwives, and nurse anesthetists.

This additional license and mandatory minimum education could also lead to a new standard of care for the advanced nurse practitioner. Although it is already true that when the care of a nurse practitioner is asserted to be negligent, in most states another nurse with the same credentials and background is called to establish the appropriate standard of care. Given the additional training and experience of the nurse practitioner, that standard is generally higher than one that would be established for a staff nurse who may have experience in the same clinical area (for example, the standard of care for a nurse midwife is higher than that for an obstetrical or perinatal nurse).

Advanced nurse practitioners must also be aware of the limits of their advanced practice. State nurse practice acts specify the appropriate scope of practice and clearly delineate the role of the advanced nurse practitioner and the importance of not performing duties that have been strictly relegated to physicians.

Under managed care, the role of health care prevention and primary care are gaining additional importance. Because in many areas of the country, there is a shortage of physicians to provide this type of care, many managed care organizations are looking to nurses who are practicing in expanded roles. Nurses working in primary care settings such as pediatric nurse practitioners, and nurse midwives may find that they have even greater opportunities to manage the care of the patients to whom they provide care. Despite the existence of treatment guidelines that are often part of managed care networks that employ advanced practitioners, nurses should be advised of the continued need to practice within the scope of their state nurse practice acts.

Also, under managed care systems, nurses are working in positions such as utilization managers. In this capacity, a nurse may be in the position to influence decisions about the type of treatment that a patient is to receive because of the level of reimbursement that has been approved. Although the nurse who manages utilization may be utilizing clinical protocols to deny care, what should be realized is that the nurse is not actually denying the care, but rather is denying reimbursement for that care. The physician continues to have the responsibility to provide appropriate and necessary care and treatment to patients and to appeal the decision to not reimburse for that care provided.

EXAM QUESTIONS

CHAPTER 1
Questions 1–14

1. What is the term used to describe a situation in which a person fails to do something that a reasonable and prudent person would do in a similar situation and that act harms another?

   a. battery

   b. negligence

   c. omission

   d. betrayal

2. If a nurse is found guilty of violating a criminal law, the punishment could include

   a. payment of money to the patient or family.

   b. payment of money to their employer.

   c. imprisonment and loss of licensure.

   d. payment to their insurance carrier.

3. The area of law that establishes the nurse practice acts is

   a. the Constitution.

   b. common law.

   c. the state Board of Nursing.

   d. state statutory law.

4. The area of law that addresses most issues of malpractice is

   a. the Constitution.

   b. common law.

   c. Board of Nursing.

   d. state statutes.

5. For details on how to perform your everyday nursing functions, a nurse should consult the

   a. state nurse practice act.

   b. hospital's policy and procedure manual.

   c. state legislature.

   d. state's Board of Nursing.

6. What is the term used to describe the level of care a reasonable and prudent nurse would render in a certain situation?

   a. professional ethics

   b. duty

   c. responsibility

   d. standard of care

7. Nurses are responsible for delivering a standard of care that is in keeping with

   a. what they were taught in nursing school.

   b. current standards.

   c. what was last read in a professional nursing journal.

   d. what was last learned at a seminar.

8. At trial, the court may establish the applicable standard of care by reviewing

   a. a hospital's policy and procedure manual.

   b. past cases.

   c. textbooks used in nursing school several years before.

   d. local health articles.

15

9. The first factor that a plaintiff must prove to substantiate a claim of medical malpractice is

   a. duty.
   b. standard of care.
   c. negligence.
   d. injury.

10. Which of the following would establish a nurse's duty to a patient?

    a. seeing that an unassigned patient needs help
    b. knowing about a neighbor who is sick
    c. driving by a car accident scene where someone has been injured
    d. passing the state Board of Nursing examination

11. The concept that a nurse should be able to anticipate that a patient may be injured and that she should take steps to eliminate the risk is called

    a. causation.
    b. duty.
    c. foreseeability.
    d. breach of duty.

12. If no other explanation for the patient's injury exists, the court may allow the plaintiff to prove negligence by presenting only circumstantial evidence. This theory is called

    a. respondeat superior.
    b. foreseeability.
    c. res ipsa loquitur.
    d. causation.

13. An employer is often held accountable for an employee's actions under the doctrine of

    a. res ipsa loquitur.
    b. respondeat superior.
    c. sovereign immunity.
    d. causation.

14. Hospitals may be held accountable for the actions of an agency nurse under the doctrine of

    a. respondeat superior.
    b. borrowed servant.
    c. captain-of-the-ship.
    d. res ipsa loquitur.

CHAPTER 2

COMMON SOURCES OF LIABILITY

CHAPTER OBJECTIVE

After studying this chapter, the reader will be able to identify the most common areas of liability for nurses.

LEARNING OBJECTIVES

After reading this chapter, the reader will be able to

1. describe how the courts view a nurse's role in protecting the patient from a fall.

2. describe the new policies related to the use of restraints and the nursing responsibilities associated with these new policies.

3. name the five steps a nurse needs to follow when administering medications to ensure that they are administered properly.

4. describe what should be done if a nurse feels unsure of a drug order.

5. describe the responsibilities with regard to the types of drugs nurses administer.

6. identify the differences between administering and dispensing drugs, and nursing responsibilities for each.

7. identify three major responsibilities encompassed by a nurse's duty to monitor patients.

8. identify two elements that are key to the nursing duty to notify doctors of a patient's condition.

9. discuss how a nurse could be found liable for a doctor's incompetence and the steps that should be taken to relieve that liability.

10. state how a hospital's or institution's policies and procedures manual affects nurses' legal responsibilities.

11. describe the potential liability associated with the use of clinical pathways.

You may have the impression that most medical malpractice claims originate because of some catastrophic event involving patient care. However, this is far from true. In fact, most malpractice claims against nurses stem from an error the nurse made while performing some routine function. To help you avoid such a pitfall, it is important that you become aware of the most common areas of liability affecting nurses.

FALLS

Injuries caused by falls are the most common cause of negligence lawsuits against hospitals and nurses. The courts generally expect you to use your professional judgment when evaluating patients so as to identify those patients who are at risk for falling. Such patients include those who are elderly, sedated, blind, dizzy, confused, or immediately postoperative.

If you think your patient is at risk for a fall, then you must act to minimize the risk. This may be through restraining the patient, using side rails, carefully monitoring the patient, or helping the patient whenever he needs to be out of bed. You should also make sure the patient's room is well lit and uncluttered, and that the patient wears shoes while attempting to walk. Recent changes in the law related to the use of restraints will be discussed later in this chapter.

The key here is to take precautions with any patient who you feel could accidentally fall. If you do not, you could be held liable for any injury. However, if your patient simply falls and injures himself out of the blue—without ever showing any sign of being at risk for a fall—then you probably would not be held responsible. Consider the case of *Berry v. Rapides General Hospital* (1988). In this instance, a female patient was being helped up from an examining table in the emergency room by her daughter and a nurse. When the patient's feet hit the floor, her knees buckled and she fell. At the first trial, the court stated that the hospital had a duty to protect the woman from falling. On appeal, however, the court concluded that neither the patient's history nor her physical condition indicated that she could not walk a short distance with help. The court further stated that hospitals are not required to take measures to avoid risks that a reasonable person in the same circumstances would not anticipate.

In another case, the court found that nurses don't have a duty to take precautions against a patient falling if the doctor orders otherwise. In *Carrigan v. Roman Catholic Bishop* (1962), a 55-year-old woman was in the hospital because of high blood pressure, arthritis, headaches, and chest pain. While there, she became restless and confused, and she was placed in a bed with side rails. Then, because she disturbed other patients, she was transferred to a private room, where she was monitored by a private duty nurse. After awhile, the doc-tor ordered that the side rails be removed, and the private duty nurse was dismissed. Then, while the patient was getting out of bed to go to the bathroom, she fell. The patient sued the hospital, claiming that the nurses were negligent for complying with the doctor's order. The court disagreed. It found that there was no reason for the nurses not to comply with the doctor's order to remove the patient's side rails. In addition, it stated that the night nurse did not have a duty to constantly watch a sleeping patient.

Recent changes in the law associated with the use of restraints can create confusion in the appropriate management of patients who may require the use of restraints. Federal law under the auspices of the Health Care Financing Administration (HCFA) has recently adopted a "functional approach" to the definition of restraints which has resulted in new regulations. In promulgating this new regulation, HCFA has stated:

"We have adopted a functional definition that does not name each device and situation that can be used to inhibit an individual's movement simply because we believe that this approach is counterproductive. One could not possibly capture all scenarios or devices in regulation, and a functional approach promotes looking at individual situations. From our experience with nursing homes, we know that many people look for a clear-cut list of restraints. We believe that clinicians will agree, however, that each case is different. A device that acts as a restraint for one individual may not inhibit the movement of another. Accordingly, we have incorporated a definition that focuses on function for the individual" (Federal Register, 1999). In summary, this informs hospitals that the casual, automatic use of restraints, too long the practice in many hospitals, will no longer be accepted by the federal government.

With the possible consequences being so serious, hospitals must build the least-restrictive restraint practice programs that help health care providers to promote quality care, support individual uniqueness, foster knowledge and professionalism.

As a practicing nurse, you can probably think of at least five situations when you believe the use of restraints might be appropriate: 1) to manage threatening behavior toward others or self, 2) to maintain therapies and prevent removal of tubes, 3) to curtail the activities of patients who wander into other patients rooms, 4) to prevent the confused patient from climbing out of bed, falling and injuring himself, and 5) as a punitive measure, to enforce patient compliance. All of these possible situations should be re-evaluated in light of recent legislative changes.

In July 1999, a patient's rights bill was debated in the Senate for four days, and the Health Care Financing Administration (HCFA) has implemented six new patient protection standards that all hospitals must have met by August 2, 1999, in order to participate in the Medicare and Medicaid programs.

Restraint for Acute Medical and Surgical Care—this standard applies to restraints used for medical and surgical treatment as distinguished from behavior management. In the conditions of participation (CoP), a physical restraint includes equipment adjacent to the patient's body that the patient cannot easily remove. The comments state that side rails are a restraint. Also, restraints may be physical or chemical. Drug restraint is any medication that controls behavior or restricts movement and is not standard treatment for the patient's medical or psychiatric condition.

Seclusion and Restraint for Behavior Management—this is the most troublesome of all the standards in this new regulation.

Summarized, this section states that restraints must be:

* implemented in the least restrictive manner possible

* in accordance with safe appropriate restraining techniques

* must be ended at the earliest possible time

* The patient who is restrained or in seclusion must continually be assessed, monitored, and reevaluated.

* All staff who have direct patient contact must have ongoing education and training in the proper and safe use of seclusion and restraint application and techniques and alternative methods for handling behavior, symptoms, and situations that in the past have been treated through the use of restraints or seclusion

* The hospital or other health care facility must report to HCFA any death that occurs while a patient is restrained or in seclusion, or where it is assumed that a patient's death is a result of restraint or seclusion. A restraint and seclusion may not be used simultaneously unless the patient is:

1. continually monitored *face-to-face* by an assigned staff member; or

2. continually monitored by staff using both video and audio equipment. This monitoring must be in close proximity to the patient. HCFA's restraint and seclusion standards (section VI) represent the most significant change for hospitals and were patterned after the JCAHO requirements, which were revised in September 1998 and became effective in January 1999. Together with the National Association of Psychiatric Health Systems, the American Hospital Association (AHA) has sought an injunction to stop enforcement of HCFA's rule (standard VI) requiring a personal con-

sultation (face-to-face) within one hour of placing a patient in restraints or seclusion.

Nurses need to consider taking preventive measures when a patient's agitated behavior, confusion, or anxiety render him dangerous to himself or others. But restraints, are not the only option. When encountering a patient displaying difficult behavior, the nurse or other health care provider needs to first identify their concerns and evaluate the situation fully. Failure to do so could expose the nurse to liability.

The Omnibus Budget Reconciliation Act (OBRA), the Joint Commission on Accreditation of Healthcare Organizations (JCAHO) and the Health Care Financing Administration (HCFA) have all mandated strict procedures to ensure protection of patients' rights regarding physical restraint. The nurse or other health care provider must remember that their behavior will be judged against the current standard of practice, and in order for the courts to find liability, there must be evidence that standards have been ignored or violated. The nurse must also remember that litigation involving injury from restraint use is more common than are cases involving injury resulting from lack of restraint.

If restraints must be used, documentation is crucial. Documentation should include: behavior which prompted the action (behavior the patient exhibited before and after removal of restraint) as well as the alternative first employed, a physician's time-limited order indicating the date, time, and duration of use, the reason and the appropriate type of restraint obtained within the time limit designated by the institution (JCAHO recommends 12 hours), and how the patient and his family were educated regarding restraint use. The health care provider must also remember to document how often the patient was reassessed (making sure to follow the institution's policy regarding the care of patients in restraints), the removal of restraints peri-

odically, range-of-motion exercises performed, and assessment of distal pulses. Devices to be used must be approved for the purpose of restraint and must be followed according to the manufacturer's guidelines.

Should the health care provider decide not to use restraints, documentation remains equally important. Careful documentation of fall prevention strategies may be crucial during litigation and would include what exactly was done to protect the patient from harm as well as all alternatives used; this would establish that the care the patient received was consistent with the current standard of care.

A nurse can be found liable for failure to act, even in the absence of a doctor's order. This is true especially when a patient falls without protective restraints in place. In *Kujawski v. Arbor View Health Care Center* (1987), a nursing home patient fell from a wheelchair and sustained injuries. The patient was enroute to the recreation room when he was thrust forward and fell from the wheelchair. The fall caused the patient to sustain injuries to the head and arm. The plaintiff brought charges against the nursing home for failure to safely restrain the patient. The supreme court found that the nursing home and its employees were negligent in failing to use a safety belt to secure the patient in place. The fact that the doctor did not order the safety restraints did not exonerate the nurse. The court held that when restraints were used for safety and not modification of behavior, no physician order was required.

In *Bossier v. Desoto General Hospital* (1983), the court held that strict adherence to the doctor's orders could not relieve the nurse of liability. In this case, the patient was admitted for treatment of arthritis. The patient received medication for pain, which had a side effect of dizziness. During her stay in the hospital, the patient fell on two occasions. The second fall occurred within approximately one week of the first. The later fall happened as the patient attempted to go to the bathroom without the help of a nurse. At this time, no side rails or restraints were being used to prevent the patient's movement. On admission, the doctor had ordered "routine care," which included the patient to be assisted when getting out of bed. However, the doctor did not order the use of restraints or side rails to prevent the patient from getting up without assistance. In light of the nurse's awareness of the patient's use of pain medications and its side effects (dizziness) the court found that the nurse was negligent for failing to take any measures to prevent the patient from getting out of bed. The court held that the nurse should have used restraints or side rails to prevent injury. The nurse was not exonerated merely because the physician failed to specifically order these safety measures.

You also need to use your judgment when making sure that a patient's bed contains side rails and that the side rails are to be raised. If a plaintiff can prove in a lawsuit either that they were sedated to an extent that the nurses should have been aware that side rails were necessary, or that the doctor ordered side rails and they were not used, then you could be found guilty of negligence. For example, in *Smith v. West Calcasieu-Cameron Hospital* (1971), a patient received both a pain medication and a sedative. An hour later, the patient fell out of bed, fracturing a femur and sustaining a hematoma on the right temple. In the subsequent lawsuit, the court stated that, although the doctor did not order side rails, the nurses should have known that the patient needed them. The court concluded that, if the bed had contained side rails, the patient would not have fallen.

Also, beware of the patient who has a history of getting out of bed unassisted and of falling. In the case of *Keyworth v. Southern Baptist Hospitals* (1988), a 62-year-old woman who had had a stroke was famous among the nursing staff as being able to get out of her restraints within an

hour of being observed quietly sleeping. In fact, the nurses referred to the patient as "Houdini." Several precautions were taken: they had placed the patient in a room across from the nurses' station where she could be observed, the doctor ordered a Posey restraint and side rails, and the husband furnished a sitter for the evening and night shifts. Despite these things, the patient fell out of bed and fractured her hip. The court found the hospital negligent and awarded the patient more than $225,000. The court stated that the hospital was aware of the patient's tendency to get out of bed and to fall, and that the nurses should have taken extra precautions, but didn't.

In *Borne v. St. Francis Medical Center* (1995), the patient was an 81-year-old woman who became catatonic four days after discharge from back and hip surgery. The psychiatrist treated her on the psychiatric ward with medication. After her mental functioning became normal, the doctor transferred her to a rehabilitation unit to regain her strength loss due to the surgery. Because of the patient's medications, she was prone to falls. As a precaution, the nurses locked two of the patient's bed rails, placed the bed in the lowest position and placed the call bell on the bed rails.

Despite these precautions, the patient got up without assistance and fell. The nurses admonished the patient not get up without help and raised all four bed rails into the locked position. The patient again got out of bed. The nurses informed the doctor of the situation. The nurses then placed a sign within the patient's sight to remind her not to get out of bed without assistance, and used the ordered Posey vest to restrain the patient at night and when left alone. Two days later, the patient resumed getting out of bed without assistance. The nurses notified the doctor and the staff attempted to get family members to arrange for sitters to watch the patient. In the meantime, the nurses increased their efforts to prevent the patient from getting out of bed unassisted by tying the posey restraints under the bed, checking on her every fifteen minutes, and leaving her door open so the nurses could see her as they passed the room. Despite the nurses' attempts to protect the patient, the patient got out of her bed and fell. The patient fractured her skull and died eleven days later.

The patient's chart showed that the nurses failed to document the placement of the warning sign, failed to monitor the restraints and failed to monitor the patient every fifteen minutes.

However, despite the lack of documentation, other evidence showed that the nurses implemented the care described. The court found that each time the patient got out of bed, the nursing staff implemented additional safety precautions to stop the behavior. The court also found that the patient was capable of understanding and following instructions, but chose not to listen to the nurses. For those reasons, the court found that the nurses had not breached their duty to the patient.

In *LaMarca v. United States* (1998), the court held the hospital liable for the patient's fall when the nurses failed to place the patient on the Fall Risk Program. On April 11, 1994, the patient experienced dizziness and shortness of breath at the hospital's clinic. After transport to the emergency room, the hospital admitted the patient to the intensive care unit and later to the telemetry unit. At the time of the patient's admission, he was taking a diuretic, two anti-hypertensive medications, two sedatives, pain medication, and Benadryl® which lowers blood pressure and causes drowsiness. On April 12, around 11:30 a.m., the nursing staff found the patient lying on the floor of his room with a fractured hip. The nurse on duty testified that at the time of the fall, the side rails of the patient's bed were down and that the patient was not on the Fall Risk Program. At this hospital, the Fall Risk Program is an alert to all the hospital staff that a patient is at risk of falling due to illness, injury or medication. When the nursing staff places

at patient on the program, the staff must keep the patient's bed rails in the up position at all times, place a sign stating "fall risk" at the bedside, and assist the patient to the toilet every two hours. It is the duty of the registered nurse performing the admission assessment of the patient to identify whether the patient is at risk for falls.

At trial, an expert witness testified that because the patient entered the hospital due to dizziness, he was at risk for a fall. Furthermore, the cumulative effects of the sedative medications that the patient received and his medical history, which included osteoporosis and severe arthritis that decreased his mobility, increased the patient's risk for falls. Coupled with conflicting documentation and testimony, the court held that the hospital breached its duty to the patient by failing to designate him a fall risk in accordance with community standards and the hospital's own standards.

MEDICATION ERRORS

Of all the duties you perform as a nurse, administering medications may be the most risky. In an analysis of 289,411 medication orders written during one year in a tertiary care teaching hospital, the overall error rate was estimated to be 3.13 errors for each 1,000 orders written, and the rate of significant errors to be 1.81 per 1,000 orders. It has been estimated that preventable adverse events are a leading cause of death in the United States and that at least 44,000 and perhaps as many as 98,000 Americans die in hospitals each year as a result of medication errors.

As you know from nursing school, the most important steps to follow when administering medications are to make absolutely sure that you're giving the right drug, to the right patient, at the right time, in the right dosage, and by the right route. These continue to be the most important steps to follow each time you administer a drug.

As one means of reducing the number of medication errors, many hospitals have instituted the unit dose system. This is a system whereby the medications for each patient arrive from the pharmacy in individual, one time dose packages. This system has helped to decrease the number of medication errors; however, it has not eliminated them entirely. To begin with most nursing units still maintain a number of medications on the unit as part of "floor stock." And when you take a dose of medication from the floor stock to give to a patient, you can still make a mistake. In *Ciarlo v. St. Francis Hospital* (1994), the nurse went to the nursing unit floor stock area to select what she thought was Lasix®. Instead, she took out potassium instead of the Lasix. The patient died immediately after the potassium was administered. The patient's family sued the hospital and the nurse for malpractice and won. The nurse has a duty to check the medication label three times before giving the medication. The failure to do so in this case caused fatal results.

In a similar case, *Gault v. Poor Sisters of St. Francis* (1967), a nurse began to prepare a patient for a gastric cytology test. The procedure called for the nurse to give the patient a saltwater gastric lavage. By mistake, though, she lavaged the patient with diluted sodium hydroxide. The sodium hydroxide severely injured the patient internally. Both the hospital and the nurse were found liable for the injury.

Besides being responsible for the medications that you administer, you are also responsible for making sure the medication you hand the doctor is the medication requested. In *Riase v. Wood* (1988), the surgeon requested the nurse to get Xylocaine® without Epinephrine®. Instead the circulating nurse retrieved the wrong medicine, Xylocaine with Epinephrine. The physician administered the medication that was retrieved by the circulating nurse and drawn up by the scrub nurse. The Epinephrine was injected into the foot of a patient who was undergoing a bunionectomy procedure, which caused injury to the patient. The court found the nurse negligent for selecting the wrong medication. The surgeon was not held to be vicariously liable for administering the medication, since he relied on the command issued twice for the medicine to be given without the vasoconstrictor.

Another hazard of the unit dose system is that many nurses begin to take for granted that both the type and the strength of medication sent from the pharmacy are correct. You should never take this fact for granted. After all, you are responsible for any drug you give in error, even if the pharmacy sent the wrong drug. In *Gassen v. East Jefferson General Hospital* (1993), a nurse incorrectly administered a Vibramycin® 100 mg intramuscular two times a day, instead of intravenously two times a day. The plaintiff brought suit against the hospital for injuries sustained via the incorrect route of administration. The hospital filed a third-party demand against the pharmacy and its insurer. The court of appeals held that the duty of the pharmacist is limited in regards to the clarification or verification of physician prescriptions. Therefore, the pharmacist could not be held liable for the nurse's administration of a drug through the wrong route. However, the court did hold that the pharmacist could be liable if the actions taken by the pharmacist violated hospital policy dealing with drug order clarification.

The wrong dose of a medication caused the lawsuit of *Dessauer v. Memorial General Hospital* (1981). In this instance, a nurse who normally worked in obstetrics was doing relief work in the emergency room. A doctor told the nurse to give a patient 50 mg of Lidocaine®. The nurse gave 800 mg instead. The patient died as a result. The hospital—because of the nurse's action—was found guilty of malpractice.

The nurse must be certain about the dosage and frequency of a drug ordered by a doctor. Any discrepancy must be clarified with the physician. Where the nurse gives a drug in excess of the dose or more frequently than the doctor ordered by the doctor, negligence will almost always be found. In the case of *Sullivan v. Sumrall* (1993), the doctor ordered Demerol® and Dramamine® to reduce the patient's pain. The medication was ordered prn, which according to hospital policy was to be given no more frequently than every four hours. The medical record revealed that the nurse had given the patient the Demerol and Dramamine at 6:45 p.m, 10:00 p.m. and 12:25 a.m. the next morning. The last medication administered at 12:25 a.m. was given only two hours and twenty-five minutes after the patient's last medication. The hospital rules required that the nurse consult with a physician when there was a question about the dose or frequency of medication. The nurse did not contact the doctor prior to giving an additional dose. At 4:00 a.m. the patient's breathing stopped. CPR was successful; however, the patient sustained severe irreversible brain death and remains in a coma. The plaintiff brought suit against the nurse and the hospital for negligent administration of medication.

And if you are not sure about the dosage of a drug ordered by a doctor, always ask the doctor who ordered the medication. In *Norton v. Argonaut Insurance Company* (1962), the assistant director of nursing services visited the hospital's pediatrics unit while on rounds and found that the charge nurse was busy with an emergency and that the desk was full of charts containing orders that needed to be taken off. The assistant director decided to help the charge nurse by taking off the orders. In the process, she took off an order for a 3-month-old child that said, "Give 3.0 cc (ml) of Digoxin® today for one dose only." The assistant director was used to working with injectable Digoxin, not the oral elixir, and she thought that the dosage seemed excessive for such a young child. She briefly talked about the order with another registered nurse and a student. She then asked a doctor

who happened to be in the area about the dosage. The doctor, who was a consultant on the baby's case but did not order the drug, told the nurse that if that's what the other doctor had ordered, then that is what he had meant to be given. (Later, the consulting doctor claimed that he assumed that the nurse was talking about the oral form of the drug, not the injectable.) The nurse then injected the baby with 3 ml of Digoxin, which was five times the strength of the oral form of the drug. One hour later, the baby died. The nurse was held liable, as were the hospital and the doctor who prescribed the drug. The nurse's big mistake was that she did not question the doctor who had prescribed the drug about the order.

There is another factor of which you need to be certain when you give a drug. You must be certain which route of administration is the correct route. Realize that the oral dose of a drug—which is absorbed through the gastrointestinal tract—may be much larger than the dose of an injectable drug. In turn, intravenous drugs require an even smaller dosage because, with this route, the drug enters the bloodstream directly.

Another concern is that the medication is administered through the proper devices for the route of administration ordered. For example, an intravenous medication that goes directly into the blood stream and having immediate effect on the patient must be administered by an intravenous pump rather than a drip chamber. In the case of *Macon-Bibb County Hospital Authority v. Ross* (1985), Dopamine®, a medication that has immediate effects on blood pressure, was administered intravenously through a drip chamber rather than an intravenous pump. The Dopamine infiltrated into the tissues, causing severe scarring and injury to the patient's hand. The hospital was held negligent for the administration of the medication, and the failure to discover and timely treat the Dopamine infiltration. A related issue in this case is whether the infiltration of Dopamine would have been detected by an I.V. pump's alarm mechanism, thereby preventing the injury to the patient.

In another instance, a patient's medication had been changed from injectable to oral. The nurse did not pick up on the changed route, and instead drew up the oral dosage in injectable form. When she went to administer the drug to the patient, the patient told the nurse that she was making a mistake and that the route had been changed. The nurse insisted that she was right and gave the injection anyway. The lawsuit of *Larrimore v. Homeopathic Hospital* (1963) resulted, and the nurse was found guilty of malpractice.

Another lesson you should learn from the above case is to always listen to your patients. In fact, teach your patients what medications they are taking and why, and how frequently they should receive them. Furthermore, encourage the patients to question anything that seems unusual. After all, an alert patient can help prevent you—or another member of the health care team—from making a mistake.

Still another responsibility that rests on your shoulders when administering intravenous medication or intramuscular medication, is to ensure that the needle size and the injection site are appropriate. In the case of *Macon-Bibb County Hospital Authority v. Ross* (1985), the patient was admitted to the hospital for respiratory problems. Soon after being admitted to the emergency room, the patient required assisted ventilation and medicine to elevate her low blood pressure. Intravenous administration of Dopamine to elevate the patient's pressure was initiated through a small vein in the right wrist. Several hours later, the Dopamine was observed to have infiltrated into the tissues surrounding the vein, causing severe injury to the patient.

Dopamine is a potent drug that when infiltrated causes injury and possibly death to the tissues it contacts. For this reason, the standard of care is to use a large vein and to constantly monitor the site. Small veins used in emergency situations are to be changed as soon as possible to avoid injury. The court held that the site chosen for the continued administration of the Dopamine was inappropriate. It found the hospital negligent, failing to prevent the injury by not changing the site of administration to a larger vein after the emergency subsided. The hospital was also found negligent for failing to monitor the site.

In addition to being proficient in the technical aspects of administering medications, the court also holds you responsible for being familiar with all of the drugs you give. This includes being aware of side effects, signs of overdosage, safe dosage limits, and contraindications. The courts also expects you to know about any special precautions that need to be taken when administering a new drug. There is no doubt that this is a heavy responsibility, especially considering the increasing number and variety of drugs. But, in the eyes of the law, this will not excuse any lapses. As a nurse, you are responsible for knowing about the drugs you administer.

The nurse is responsible for knowing about the side effects of the drugs administered to the patients you care for. In *Hartman v. Riverside Methodist Hospital* (1989), the nurse was taking care of a patient who had undergone emergency surgery. The surgery went on without complication. However, due to the emergency nature and the immediacy of the surgical procedure, the patient had a full stomach at the time of surgery and was therefore at risk for aspiration. The consequence of aspiration into the patient's lungs is pneumonia and possible death. After the operation, the anesthesiologist informed the nurse of the patient's risk for aspirating, and requested her to monitor the patient closely. The nurse administered a narcotic to the patient after surgery without an order from the physician. The narcotic Diluadid® was administered to relieve the postoperative pain and discomfort from surgery. The Diluadid that was given to the patient combined with the Fentanyl® given during the operation and caused the patient's trachea and esophagus to relax. This relaxation allowed the stomach contents to be vomited into the lungs. The patient later died from a pneumonia that he developed subsequent to the aspiration of vomit into his lungs. The patient's family brought suit against the hospital, and the case was settled against the hospital prior to court. At trial the physician was not liable for the administration of the medication. Instead, the court found it was the duty of the nurse to know the side effects of all medications administered to the patient. This case highlights not only the need to know the side effects of the medication you administer, but also how the medications you administer are affected by other medications administered by others.

In another case—*Breit v. St. Luke's Memorial Hospital* (1987)—a nurse was held liable for injuring a patient when she administered a drug while the patient was sitting up rather than lying down. To be specific, the nurse had given a postoperative laminectomy patient an injection of Morphine Sulfate® while the patient was in bed. Afterward, the nurse helped him into a chair. The patient continued to complain of pain, and, about an hour later, the doctor ordered the nurse to give the patient another 5 mg of Morphine. The doctor wrote in his progress notes, "The MS was given to patient upright in chair. Will watch closely." Shortly after the patient received the additional 5 mg of Morphine, he lost all feeling and movement in his legs. As it turned out, the paralysis was permanent. Testimony at the trial revealed that the paralysis probably resulted when the patient developed a vascular insufficiency—a reaction to Morphine, which is considered to be classic. Experts testified that the chances of a patient having an adverse reaction to Morphine were greater if the patient was sitting up rather than lying down. The experts also testified that Morphine can cause

hypotension, dizziness, and drowsiness and should never be given to a patient who is sitting up. In finding the nurse negligent, the court stated that the nurse should have been aware of all these factors and that she breached the standard of care and exhibited poor nursing practice.

Furthermore, if you are unfamiliar with a drug, asking someone else to give it for you will not necessarily relieve you of any liability. In *Campbell v. Preston* (1964), a nurse asked an intern to inject a patient with a medication that the patient's doctor had ordered. When the intern did as the nurse requested, the patient had a cardiac arrest. The patient's family sued, and, at trial, it was revealed that only an anesthesiologist would have been qualified to give that specific medication. Even though the intern gave the drug and was also named in the lawsuit, the nurse was found negligent for not having read the literature that accompanied the drug. That literature, the court said, would have informed the nurse about the drug's special requirements.

On occasion, you may also be called upon to administer an experimental or investigational drug. If you are, be sure to find out the procedure your hospital has for giving these types of drugs. You would also need to make sure that the patient has consented, in writing, to the use of the drug. Remember that you will be the one giving the drug. For this reason, the court could hold you liable for making sure that the hospital's protocol has been followed.

Finally, you need to make sure that you understand the difference between administering a drug and dispensing a drug. The law allows nurses to administer drugs, not dispense them. Administration of a drug involves giving a single dose of a prescribed medication to a patient. Dispensation of a drug involves selecting, labeling, and packaging a drug or giving someone else a drug to administer. The problem for nurses arises when a particular drug that has been ordered is not available on the nursing unit and the pharmacist is not on duty. In this situation, the law allows you to take one dose of the prescribed medication from the pharmacy and give it to your patient. Just be aware, though, that in doing so, you will be held responsible for selecting the right drug and the right dosage for the right patient. Also, make sure that you administer the drug to the patient yourself. If you give it to another nurse to administer, you could be found guilty of unlawfully dispensing a drug. Also, do not take an empty container from your nurses' station and fill it with a drug. This, too, would be considered dispensing a drug.

Besides all of these responsibilities, you do have some rights. For example, if you think that a prescribed drug will harm a patient because the prescribed dosage is too high or because it is con-traindicated for some reason, then you have a legal right to refuse to give the drug. If you do refuse, make sure you notify your immediate supervisor—so that she can clarify the order or attempt to remedy the situation in some other way—as well as the prescribing doctor. Depending on your hospital's policy, you may also need to document why you did not give the drug.

BURNS

Another extremely common area of negligence attributed to nurses are burns. Burns can occur from a variety of sources, including hot water bottles, heating pads, sitz baths, vaporizers, and douches. Because of the risk of burning a patient, you should check your hospital's policy and procedure manual before using any device that could potentially cause a burn.

Besides your risk of being held liable for burning a patient during a procedure, you could also be held responsible if your patient burns himself after spilling a hot liquid. While this would not be an act of negligence under normal situations, it would be

if the court feels that the patient should not have been handling the liquid in the first place. The best examples of this would be if the patient was elderly, young, sedated, or confused.

For example, in *Striano v. Deepdale General Hospital* (1976), an 11-year-old boy was in the hospital following a tonsillectomy. The doctor ordered a diet of milk, ice cream, and Jello®. Because it was more convenient, the nurse requested that a complete liquid diet be sent from the kitchen. She knew that a complete liquid diet would contain other foods besides milk, ice cream, and Jello®, but she planned to simply remove any of these items before the child ate them. When the tray arrived, it also contained hot water for tea. The nurse placed the tray in front of the child and, before she could remove the tea pot, the boy knocked it over. The hot water splashed on his ankle and burned it. The court ruled that the nurse had acted contrary to the doctor's instructions and that she was liable for the burn.

Emory University v. Porter (1961) relates an incident involving an incubator. The incubator contained a light bulb that, when the cover was placed on the incubator, was obstructed from view. Hospital policy directed nurses to either remove the bulb or turn it off whenever the incubator was in use. However, in this instance, a nurse placed an infant in the incubator without doing either. The baby's foot pressed against the bulb and was seriously burned. As a result, three-fourths of the infant's foot had to be amputated. The parents originally tried to sue the baby's doctor, but the court stated that the doctor wasn't responsible. The case was then sent back for trial against the hospital and the nurse.

During operating procedures, patients are sometimes placed upon heating pads. It is often the duty of the nurse to set up the heating pad prior to the operation and to observe the patient's skin during the operation. The nurse can be liable for burns if they result from failure to set up the heating pad correctly or from failure to observe the skin for potential burns. In the case of *Smelko v. Brinton and Wichita, Inc.* (1987), a 3-month-old child sustained burns after he underwent surgery for an inguinal hernia. During the operation the child was placed on the heating pad. Upon waking up from the surgery the child screamed in pain. The recovery room nurses failed to observe any blisters or other signs of burns. However, when the mother got home she removed the diaper and observed large blisters and burns on the child's skin. On later exam it was discovered that the child had second and third-degree burns over 75% of his buttocks. The pad had been set up by the circulating nurse. The plaintiff brought charges against the surgery center, the doctor and the anesthesiologist. All defendants admitted liability, and the child was awarded $400,000 and the parent's were awarded $2,250. This case highlights the nurse's need to observe the operating room patient who is placed on a heating pad.

The nurse has a duty to protect the patient from harm. In the case of *Beckham v. St. Paul Fire and Marine Insurance Company* (1993), the patient had undergone a repair of a hernia and an abdominoplasty or tummy tuck. After surgery, the patient had been given Demerol® to control pain as well as a heating pad, as ordered by the doctor, to relieve the patient's pain as needed. After surgery the patient was not aware of where she was or what time it was. She exhibited confused behavior in that she had played with her dressings and the heating pad. The patient was confused and receiving Demerol, which caused the patient to have reduced stimuli to pain from a burn. This made it even more important to monitor the patient closely. Nevertheless, sometime after placement of the heating pad, blisters and severe burns were observed at the site where the heating pad was located. The damage to the area of skin caused the patient's incision to open. The plaintiff sued the hospital for the nurse's

negligence in failing to observe and prevent harm to the patient. The hospital settled out of court. In this case, it was determined that the nurse's negligence was a direct cause of the patient's injuries. In this case, it appears that the nurse had an increased duty due to the state of mind of the patient and the effect of the pain medication.

The nurse must always check the patient when on a heating pad even if the patient refuses to be examined. Typically, a patient is capable of telling the nurse when the heating pad is causing a burn to the skin. In such a case, the nurse must discontinue treatment. There are times, however, when the patient will not be able to sense when a burn is occurring. For example, if the patient is given pain medication such as in the case of *Hackathorn v. Lester E. Cox Medical Center* (1992), the patient will not be able to sense the burns to the skin. In this case a heating pad was placed under the patient and was left there for over a day. The nurses did not follow protocol and failed to check the condition of the skin because the patient refused to turn. Later, when the heating pad was removed, the patient was found to have blisters and severe burns on his back. The plaintiff brought suit against the nurse and the hospital for failing to observe the condition of the skin. The fact that the patient refused to turn was no defense. When factors contribute to reducing the patient's ability to feel painful sensation, the nurse cannot rely on the patient's assessment of how his skin feels. The nurse must independently conduct an assessment of the patient's skin.

Again, the bottom line is that you are responsible for protecting your patients from injury, and this includes injuries from burns. Be alert for possible sources of burns and take action to prevent a burn from occurring. And, of course, always use your nursing skills to identify patients who run the risk of being burned.

FAILURE TO OBSERVE

As a nurse, one of your greatest responsibilities is to assess and monitor your patients. This is a very broad area and includes performing necessary assessments—whether ordered or whether, in your professional judgment, they are necessary—and reporting any changes to the doctor.

An example of the repercussions of such an omission is chronicled in the landmark case of *Darling v. Charleston Memorial Hospital* (1965). In this case, an 18-year-old male entered the hospital emergency room after breaking his leg playing football. The doctor in the emergency room set and cast the patient's leg. Almost immediately, the patient began complaining of severe pain. His toes became swollen and dark and then turned cold and insensitive. Although these are obvious signs of circulation impairment, the nurses only checked the condition a few times a day. And then, they did not report their findings to anyone. The day after the cast was applied, the doctor notched the cast around the patient's toes. The day after that, the doctor used a Stryker® saw to split the sides of the cast. In the process of splitting the cast, the doctor cut the boy's leg on both sides. The wounds began to ooze blood and a foul-smelling discharge. Again, the nurses failed to pick up on the seriousness of the situation. The patient eventually transferred to another hospital, where the admitting doctor immediately realized that the boy's leg contained a considerable amount of necrotic tissue caused by the tight cast. Despite several surgical attempts to save the leg, the doctor eventually had to amputate it. The court found that the nurses at the first hospital had failed to adequately monitor the patient's toes for color, temperature, and movement. The court also found the nurses negligent for not notifying the doctor of the patient's changing condition.

A nurse has a duty to observe and properly assess patients for symptoms or changes that are indicative of deterioration. The physician relies on the nurse's observations in order to effectively treat and diagnose the patient's condition. When the nurse fails to observe important symptoms or changes in the condition of the patient, negligence can be found.

In *Odom v. Louisiana Dept. of Health & Hospital* (1999), the patient was a fourteen year old non-verbal male with the mental age of two months. The patient suffered from spastic quadriplegia, hydocephalus, asthma, seizures and respiratory distress. Because the patient's airway was malformed, he was dependent upon his tracheostomy tube for breathing. As a result of this malformation, the patient required monitoring per an apnea monitor.

At the long-term care facility, the staff implemented a plan that required the apnea monitor to be in the operational mode when the patient was asleep or unattended, and that a spare tracheotomy tube maintained at the bedside. The facility also implemented an apnea monitor chart for the nurses to fill out on a daily basis. The facility implemented this charting system because the nurses would turn off the monitor out of frustration (the monitor would frequently alarm without cause or the patient would breath hold to gain attention).

In August 1994, the nursing staff found the patient with his trach tube out of his stoma. The patient was cyanotic and unresponsive. The spare trach tube was not located at the patient's bedside. The staff initiated CPR, without success.

The court upheld the doctrine of respondeat superior finding the hospital liable for the negligent acts of the nursing staff. The court found that the staff failed to monitor the patient, and the hospital failed to instruct, train and supervise its employees. Furthermore, the court found that the disappearance of the apnea monitor and trach care check lists raised the presumption that the nursing staff turned off the apnea monitor.

In *McMunn v. Mount Carmel Health* (1998), the patient was a 39-year-old male who entered the hospital because of severe pain caused by a kidney stone. At 4:35 p.m. in the Emergency Room, the patient received five milligrams (mg) of Morphine for pain intravenously. His oxygen saturation at that time was ninety-six percent. By 5:00 p.m., the patient had received two more 5 mg doses of Morphine. At that time, the patient's oxygen saturation was at ninety-four percent. At 6:20 p.m., the patient had received three more 5 mg doses of Morphine. His oxygen saturation had decreased to eighty-six percent, which is abnormal. The nursing staff placed the patient on oxygen. At 7:35 p.m., the patient's oxygen saturation had increased to ninety-four percent, and the patient received 1 mg of Dilaudid® (Dilaudid is a narcotic similar to morphine, the dose received by the patient was equivalent to 7 mg of Morphine).

At 8:15 p.m., the doctor transferred the patient to the hospital ward. The hospital's policy after intravenous narcotic administration is to monitor for respiratory depression every hour for twenty-four hours. On the evening shift, the patient never had his vital signs taken on the ward. Moreover, after his transfer to the ward at 10:30 p.m., the patient received an additional 15 mgs of Morphine with 50 mgs of Phenergan® (Phenergan relieves nausea and potentiates the central nervous system effects of narcotics). At 1:05 a.m., the night shift found the patient in respiratory and cardiac arrest. Despite CPR efforts, the patient died.

The court found that the nurses' failure to monitor the patient's vital signs constituted a breach of standard of care as set by hospital policy. In addition, the court also found that the nurses' failure to assess, monitor, and document the care of the patient receiving narcotics were a breach of the general standards of nursing care.

In *Erby v. North Mississippi Medical Center* (1995), the patient had a thirty year history of insulin dependent diabetes, and as a result had developed chronic renal failure. On August 26, 1987, the patient entered the hospital for the surgical creation of an AV fistula for kidney dialysis. Three days after the procedure, the patient became disoriented and comatose. The patient later died on September 3, 1987. The plaintiff sued the hospital for failing to monitor the patient's blood glucose after surgery. Hospital records showed that the nurses had not monitored the patient's blood glucose from the hours of 11:00 a.m. until 8:15 p.m. on August 29, 1987 despite the presence of a standing hospital order. Per deposition, the doctor testified that the patient's death was caused by insufficient insulin that precipitated a diabetic coma. The court held that the evidence showing that the nurses had deviated from acceptable standards of care, gave the plaintiff the right to proceed with the case.

You also have a duty to recognize when you need to monitor a patient even more closely than is ordered, such as when the patient's condition deteriorates or changes. An example where nurses failed to do so is described in the case of *Duren v. Suburban Community Hospital* (1985). The patient was a 47-year-old man who was admitted to the hospital for complaints of stomach pain, nausea, and vomiting. He was obese at 300 pounds, and he had a history of diabetes and pancreatitis. On admission, the doctor ordered an EKG; several blood tests, including serum calcium; tests for urine glucose four times a day; and sliding scale insulin to be given according to the urine glucose results. At 10:00 p.m., the patient complained of pain, had a pulse rate of 144, and a temperature of 102°F. Regardless, the nurse did not call the patient's doctor and, at shift change, did not tell the night nurse about the patient's situation. As it turned out, the nurse did not call a doctor at all until 5:00 a.m., and then she only called the house doctor to restart the patient's I.V., which had come out while the patient was thrashing in bed. The house doctor did not come until almost 7:00 a.m. Just 17 minutes later, the patient was pronounced dead. The chart revealed that no one had taken any vital signs on the patient, and no one had given him any pain medication, until 5:00 a.m. Also, the EKG was never done; only one urine glucose was performed, and, although the result showed a high level of glucose, no insulin was given. The calcium result was not available until after the patient died. Then, in court, evidence showed that the 6:00 a.m. nurses' notes were fabricated, and that the night nurse signed them even though she had not written them. The jury awarded the patient's wife $2.5 million for wrongful death and $500,000 for pain and suffering.

In *Belmon v. St. Francis Cabrini Hospital* (1983), a medical technician performed a venipuncture on a patient who was receiving Heparin® therapy at 5:00 a.m. Immediately afterward, the patient began complaining of pain above and below his elbow, which was the area where the blood sample had been taken. Although the nurse was aware of the patient's complaints, she did not call the doctor until 11:50 a.m. When the doctor arrived at noon, he discovered a large hematoma on the patient's arm. Despite the fact that the doctor wrapped and elevated the arm, and reduced the Heparin® dosage, the patient suffered permanent nerve damage. The court later found the medical technician liable for not taking necessary precautions when performing a venipuncture on a heparinized patient, and the nurse liable for failing to recognize and respond to signs of hemorrhaging.

Another case that involved the allegation that the nurses failed to recognize the development of a serious condition is *Utter v. United Hospital Center, Inc.* (1977). In this instance, the patient had been admitted to the hospital with a comminuted compound fracture of the right wrist, a posterior dislocation of the right elbow, and a compression fracture of the second lumbar vertebra after having

fallen from a ladder. A cast was applied to his arm, extending from above the elbow to below the knuckles of the right hand. The patient's arm became swollen, black, very edematous, and began emitting a foul-smelling drainage. The patient's temperature began to climb, and he was occasionally delirious. On the third day after his admission, the charge nurse called the patient's doctor; however, she did not give the doctor all of the pertinent information. She told the doctor that the patient could not keep down his oral antibiotics, but she did not tell him about the delirium or about the drainage. The patient's condition continued to worsen and, later that night, the patient transferred to another hospital. There, despite vigorous treatment, his arm had to be amputated at the shoulder. In the subsequent lawsuit, the court found that the nurses had failed to properly care for the patient. They did not recognize the developing complication and, consequently, did not seek the treatment needed. The court made it clear that nurses are obligated to take some positive action if the patient's condition shows signs of worsening. To be exact, the court stated, "In the dim hours of the night, as well as in the light of day, nurses are charged with the duty to observe the condition of the ill and infirm in their care. If that patient, helpless and wholly dependent, shows signs of worsening, the nurse is charged with the obligation of taking positive action."

And, if a physician is not doing a proper job, your duty to monitor could become even more intense. In *Fincke v. Peeples* (1985), a 17-year-old boy had a repair of a torn medial meniscus. Both the surgeon and the anesthesiologist accompanied the patient to the recovery room. As the surgeon was leaving the room, the anesthesiologist placed his hand over the endotracheal tube to determine the depth of the patient's respirations. At that time, the patient was still heavily sedated and was not moving or fighting the tube. When the surgeon returned to the recovery room after talking with the boy's parents, he found that the patient had been extubated. The anesthesiologist was gone, but the nurse told the surgeon that everything was fine and that the patient was sleeping. The surgeon left, and the nurse went to care for another patient. After several minutes, she realized that the boy's heart had stopped. Despite resuscitation efforts, the patient never regained consciousness and died about two weeks later.

At the trial, the anesthesiologist testified that his notes stated that the patient had entered the recovery room at 10:50 a.m. At 11:30 a.m., he had noted that the patient "bucked and coughed on tube. Turned head—pulled out because patient could not tolerate tube." The nurse, however, stated that that was not the case. To prove her point, she said that she had inserted an oral airway in the boy's mouth after he had been extubated and that he had not resisted. She stated that if he had been conscious at all, he would have resisted the insertion of the oral airway.

The trial revealed that the nurses in the recovery room had complained repeatedly—both in staff meetings and to the head of the anesthesiology department—about this particular anesthesiologist's tendency to extubate patients too soon. But, instead of this helping to exculpate the nurse from blame, it actually made her more liable. This is because the nurse knew this anesthesiologist tended to extubate his patients before they could breathe well. She also recognized the fact that this patient was not yet awake. Therefore, she was obligated to observe the patient closely and to either stimulate the patient to breathe or, if necessary, to have him reintubated. The jury awarded the family more than $1 million, which included punitive damages because of the hospital's gross negligence.

Remember that, above all, your first duty is to the patient. Include all parts of the nursing process in your patient care, and monitor the patient closely for any change in status or any sign of a complication. Use your nursing knowledge to make nursing diagnoses and to form a clinical opinion. If you feel the patient needs closer monitoring, then you have a duty to see that it is given.

FAILURE TO NOTIFY THE DOCTOR

Along with your responsibility to appropriately monitor a patient's condition, you have a duty to communicate any pertinent information to the doctor. Granted, this is often easier said than done, especially if several physicians are treating the same patient. In this instance, you should first call the specialist if a problem concerns a particular area (such as calling the consulting nephrologist if the patient has a decreased urine output). But remember, the attending physician retains total responsibility for the patient.

You must also remain alert and use your best judgment as to when to notify a doctor. You cannot wait an unnecessarily long time before notifying the doctor about a change in the patient's status, and you must be diligent in your efforts to actually speak with the doctor—not just leave messages. Of course, the nurse must not spend so much time attempting to contact the physician that patient care becomes compromised. When repeated attempts to contact a physician are unsuccessful, the nurse should call the nursing or hospital administrator who should then assume responsibility for contacting an appropriate physician to intervene.

A nurse has an obligation to notify the physician when the condition of the patient changes. A physician relies on the nurse's proper assessments and requires timely notification of changes in the assessments in order to intervene and provide treatment. Failure to notify the physician may cause delays in the diagnosis and treatment and negatively affect the outcome of the patient's condition.

In the case of *George v. LDS Hospital* (1990), a patient underwent a hysterectomy on July 30, 1986. The surgery went well. However, postoperatively the patient experienced difficulty with her breathing. A blockage in the lung was suspected, and the patient was transferred to the intensive care unit. The patient was later sent for a pulmonary angiogram. The test was completed and showed no blockage.

Upon return to the intensive care unit, the patient exhibited a change in mental status. She was confused, agitated, and had more difficulty breathing than before the test. All of these symptoms could have been attributed to low levels of oxygen or hypoxia. At 3:00 p.m., the attending physician was notified of the patient's return from the test. The results of the test were discussed with the doctor. However, no mention of the patient's changing condition was discussed.

From 3:00 p.m. until 7:00 p.m., the patient's condition continued to deteriorate, both physically and mentally. The nurses and the residents observed and made notation of the changing condition, yet the attending physician was not notified. At 7:00 p.m., the patient stopped breathing. Resuscitation efforts were successful in bringing back the patient's pulse. However, there was evidence that the patient did not receive assisted ventilation for up to 13 minutes after the breathing first stopped. Consequently, the patient sustained severe irreversible brain damage and then died two days later after a second cardiac arrest.

The plaintiff brought a wrongful death action against the hospital and the doctors for failure to observe and treat the patient's changing condition. The jury found the doctors not liable and attributed 100% of the negligence to the hospital, for the nurse's and resident's failure to observe and notify the attending physician of the patient's changing condition. However, the issue of proximate cause was appealed, as the jury found no proximate cause

between the delay and the death of the patient. The appellate disagreed. It concluded that a reasonable jury could find that the proximate cause of the patient's death was the nurse's failure to notify the doctor since such inaction prevented timely diagnosis and life-saving treatment.

Consider also the case of *Robert v. Chodoff* (1978). Here, the nurses were negligent on a number of issues, only one of which was failure to notify the patient's doctor. The patient had been hospitalized for a transthoracic vagotomy, after which his surgeon ordered that vital signs be taken every 15 minutes for one hour and then every hour for 10 hours. Despite this, the patient's vital signs were only recorded four times the entire day. Also, at one point, the patient asked the nurse to change his bandage. The nurse, however, was in a hurry to go to dinner, so she simply took some Kleenex® belonging to another patient and stuffed it down into the incision.

The next day, the patient's temperature climbed over 102°F at noon. At 4:00 p.m., it was 101.4°F. The nurses did not take another temperature until 8:00 a.m. the next morning, when it was 105.2°F. The nurse administered some aspirin and, at 10:45 a.m., the patient's temperature registered 106°F. The nurse finally contacted a resident, who examined the patient and found signs of a serious wound infection. When the patient's surgeon arrived between 1:00 p.m. and 2:00 p.m., the patient's condition was critical. Despite vigorous and prolonged treatment, the patient suffered irreversible organic brain syndrome as a direct result of his infection and high temperature. An expert testified at trial that the longer an elevated temperature exists, the greater the chances of developing organic brain syndrome. The court found that the nurses breached the standard of care when they failed to notify a doctor of the patient's exceedingly high temperature of 105°F. The jury awarded the patient $800,000 because of the nurses' negligence.

However, be aware that even if you assess the patient as ordered, and record your observations, you may still be negligent if you do not verbally notify the doctor of any abnormalities. This is exactly what happened in the case of *Sandhofer v. Abbott-Northwestern Hospital* (1979). The patient was admitted to the hospital for a fractured wrist, to which a cast was applied. For five days, the nurses followed the doctor's orders to monitor the circulation in the patient's fingers and duly recorded their observations. The problem was that they found the patient's fingers to be anything from "bluish and cool" to "edematous and cyanotic." The nurses were concerned about these findings; however, they did not notify the doctor. By the time the doctor became aware of the problem and split the cast, the patient's hand had become markedly ischemic. In the end, the patient's arm had to be amputated just below the elbow. The patient sued, and the court found that the nurses were the direct cause of the amputation because they failed to notify the doctor of the circulatory impairment.

In addition to your responsibility to notify a doctor of certain situations, you also have a duty to give the doctor all of the pertinent information needed to make a diagnosis. In *Hodges v. Effingham County Hospital Authority* (1981), the patient visited the hospital's emergency department complaining of stomach pain. No doctor was present in the emergency department, but the nurses called the doctor on-call. Based on the information the nurses gave him, the doctor decided to discharge the patient. Later that morning, the patient visited the office of another doctor, where she suffered a cardiac arrest and later died. As it turned out, the patient had a history of a heart condition and had even told the nurses that she had taken a nitroglycerine tablet before coming to the emergency department. However, the nurses did not give that information to the doctor. They also did not question the patient further to discover that she took several other drugs, one of which was Quinidine®, a heart medication. The court stated that it was clearly the nurses' responsibility to obtain this type of information and convey it to the doctor, and that the doctor had a right to rely on the nurses to carry out this responsibility.

Remember, both patients and doctors depend on your professional skills and judgment. If you notice a change in the patient's condition of which the doctor needs to be aware, then you need to let the doctor know—right then, not 10 hours later. At the same time, you need to use your interviewing and observation skills to gather all of the information the doctor may need to make a decision regarding the patient's treatment.

THE DOCTOR'S FAILURE TO RESPOND

As you probably already know, it can sometimes be difficult to make sure that your patient receives the care that they need. For example, what if you notify the doctor of a change in a patient's status, but the doctor does not respond? Could you be held responsible? The answer is, yes.

The bottom line is that your highest duty is to the welfare of the patient. If you feel that a doctor's order contains a discrepancy or is in error, or if you feel the patient needs care that is not being given, you have a duty to call it to the doctor's attention. If the doctor does not respond in a satisfactory manner, then you should notify your supervisor, the hospital administrator, medical director or the chairman of that doctor's department. For example, in *Utter v. United Hospital Center* (1977), which was discussed under the previous heading, the nurses were negligent for failing to recognize the seriousness of the situation. But they were also negligent because they did not make sure that the patient received the care needed, despite the doctor's inaction.

When a physician fails to respond, the nurse has an independent duty to the patient to act for the well-being of the patient. Following the doctor's orders does not relieve the nurse of liability.

In *NKC Hospitals, Inc. v. Anthony* (1993), the patient was admitted to an obstetrical unit with symptoms of nausea, vomiting, and gastric pain. The nurse started an I.V., administered anti-nausea medication, and performed tests as ordered by the physician. Approximately two hours later, the doctor was notified with the results of the tests and with information that the patient was in severe pain. The doctor wrote discharge orders, which included medication for what he diagnosed as a urinary tract infection. Fifteen minutes later, the nurse notified the physician that the patient's severe pain continued. At this time the nurse informed the doctor that she did not agree to discharging the patient. The nurse notified her supervisor of her reservations with regard to the condition and discharge of the patient. Despite the nurse's concerns and evaluations, the doctor insisted on discharge and ordered medication for pain. The patient experienced some relief after the pain medication was administered. However, at the time of discharge the patient was still in pain. No additional physician was notified or contacted to re-evaluate the condition of the patient. The patient was readmitted to the hospital four hours later. Subsequently, it was found that the patient experienced a perforated appendix and unfortunately later died of complications.

The court found that the hospital was negligent for failing to detect the perforated appendix on first admission. Despite the nurse's obvious efforts to prevent the discharge, the court found the hospital and the actions of the nurse to be negligent. Following the doctor's orders was not an appropriate defense. In light of the nurse's own doubts about the patient's condition at discharge, the court held that the nurse had an independent duty to investigate and follow up the risks involved. Notification of an additional physician to re-evalu-

ate the condition of the patient might have relieved the nurse and hospital of liability.

The nurse has a duty to inform the physician promptly of any abnormal symptoms or changes in the patient's condition. If the nurse fails to inform the physician of symptoms, liability can be imposed for injuries resulting from the delayed notification. In *Berdyck v. Shinde* (1991), the patient was admitted to the hospital's obstetrical unit at approximately 3:12 a.m. At that time, the patient's blood pressure read 196/112. A repeat blood pressure which was 192/118, was checked by the RN after administering medication. The nurse notified the physician regarding test results and the patient's elevated blood pressure readings. The physician was notified at 4:00 a.m. regarding the patient's high blood pressure and laboratory tests. The doctor ordered the nurse to observe the patient closely and to call him at any time. No medication was ordered. The nurse had observed the patient to have difficulty urinating, a right-sided headache, epigastric pain, and irregular but palpable contractions, which are associated with a pre-eclampsia condition. These symptoms were not reported to the physician at the time of the telephone call. The nurse took another blood pressure reading at 4:05 a.m. which was 192/112. No additional pressure readings were taken, and the doctor was not notified. At 4:30 a.m. the patient was observed to be resting comfortably in bed; however, at 5:15 a.m. the patient had an eclamptic grand mal seizure. The plaintiff brought an action against the hospital for the nurse's failure to make reasonable nursing assessments and the failure to take steps to prevent the eclamptic seizure. The court held that the nurse has a duty to the patient to prevent harm to the patient and to notify the physician of any abnormal symptoms. The court found if the doctor had been notified, magnesium sulfate could have been ordered and prevented the seizure. The court concluded that the nurse was negligent in performing her duty to observe and her duty to follow the doctor's orders.

A case where the doctor's care was obviously negligent, but the nurse was also found negligent for failing to disclose, was *Edwards v. Our Lady of Lourdes Hospital* (1987). In this case, a premature infant was admitted to the neonatal intensive care unit (NICU) on the evening shift. A graduate nurse, who was caring for the infant, assisted a surgical resident in performing a cutdown for an I.V. in the infant's femoral area. Although a reasonably prudent nurse should have known that a femoral cutdown is contraindicated in a premature infant, and although the graduate nurse was aware that the pulses in that leg were diminished, she didn't say anything to the resident. At shift change, the nurse coming on duty felt that the resident had placed the I.V. line in the artery, not the vein. She noted that the infant's foot was blanched and that blood pulsed back in the I.V. line whenever she tried to connect it to the I.V. solution. Despite repeated requests to the resident to come and look at the line, the resident refused. He told her that "she did not know what she was talking about." This nurse contacted her supervisor; however, the supervisor told the nurse to talk to the resident and not to call the attending neonatologist or the director of the NICU. Throughout the course of the shift, hyperalimentation was hooked up to the cutdown line. By the next morning, the nurse coming on duty took one look at the leg and immediately called the director of the NICU and a vascular surgeon. The doctors diagnosed the infant as having gangrene in his leg. They took the infant to surgery, where they attempted to re-establish blood flow to the infant's leg. However, the gangrene spread, and the infant's right leg was amputated at hip level along with one-half of his buttocks.

While all of this may put you into a panic that you are going to be held liable because of a doctor's mistake, you should note this: Most courts will not hold you responsible for any harm that comes to a patient if you are simply following the doctor's order. However, if the doctor's order clearly goes against common practice, and a reasonably prudent nurse should know that, then you could be liable. If such a situation occurs, you have a duty to question the doctor about the order, and even pursue the matter to higher authorities if necessary. It may be uncomfortable for you to do so at the time, but always remember that you have a legal responsibility to use your professional judgment to protect the patient.

VIOLATION OF POLICIES AND PROCEDURES

Every hospital has a policies and procedures manual for nurses. As an employee of that institution, you are responsible for knowing the policies and following the procedures. At the same time, however, you are obligated to follow your professional standards. At times this may put you in conflict with the institution's policies or procedures. However, the best manuals have a certain amount of leeway built in, so that you can evaluate specific situations and act accordingly.

Keep in mind that courts tend to rule against nurses who violate their hospital's policies and subsequently injure a patient. If you violate an established policy, the court will most likely say that you breached your duty. At the same time, hospitals have a responsibility to have appropriate policies and procedures in place. A case where the nurses were found guilty of not following established policy and the hospital was found deficient in their policies was *Campbell v. Pitt County Memorial Hospital* (1987).

In this case, a woman was admitted to the hospital for delivery of an infant. Both the doctor and the nurses on duty knew that the baby was in the footling breech position (with the feet presenting first). In fact, several hours before delivery, the nurses were aware of complications resulting from the presentation, and they felt that the fetus was being harmed. One nurse voiced her concerns to the doctor, but no one notified the supervisor. Throughout this entire process, no one informed the patient or her husband of the baby's position or explained the significance of that position. The parents were never given the option of having a Cesarean section delivery, and the doctor chose to proceed with a vaginal delivery. During the course of the delivery, the umbilical cord became wrapped around the infant's legs, cutting off necessary blood supply to the infant. As a result, the baby sustained severe brain damage for which she requires constant care.

The nurses erred, first of all, because the hospital had a policy that a consent must be obtained from a patient before any procedures are performed. This included obtaining a consent before the delivery of a child. However, no one ever gave the parents a consent form to sign, and none of the nurses checked to see if the parents had signed a consent. The nursing expert at trial testified that, while it's the doctor's responsibility to explain the risks of procedures, it's the nurse's responsibility to assure that the patient has received such an explanation. Both parents stated that if anyone had explained the risks of a vaginal delivery as opposed to a Cesarean section, they would have definitely opted for a Cesarean section.

The nurse was also negligent because she knew that the doctor was not responding appropriately to the fetus' distress, and yet she failed to notify her supervisor or anyone else. In part, though, this was the hospital's fault. The court found that the hospital was negligent for not having an effective procedure in place for reporting such situations.

Another case where the nurse was found negligent for failing to follow hospital policies was *St. Elizabeth Hospital v. Graham* (1994). In this case, the patient was admitted to the hospital for treat-

ment of a head injury. The patient was placed in a wheelchair without restraints or a Posey vest, despite the patient's disoriented, confused and combative mental status. Additionally, the nursing staff was aware that the patient experienced coordination problems. Unrestrained, the patient fell out of the chair and suffered further injuries, which aggravated his previous condition. It was the policy of the hospital that the application of safety restraints, such as a Posey, was left to the nurses' discretion. The policy included restraining patients who were confused, disoriented, or without sufficient physical control to protect themselves from falling. The court held that the policy on restraints was for the purpose of patient safety. It found the nurse negligently failed to follow hospital policy, causing the injuries to the patient.

In conclusion, you should review your hospital's policies and procedures at frequent intervals and make sure that your care is in accordance with those policies. The only time you should refuse to follow hospital policy is if that policy conflicts with your nurse practice act. Also, be alert for policies that are out-of-date or impractical. Suggest changes, where appropriate, at departmental staff meetings or conferences. If you would like a more direct response, you can follow your hospital's grievance procedure or contact your hospital's management committee regarding changes you feel should be made.

DEFECTIVE EQUIPMENT

Because you probably handle the equipment used in patient care more than anyone else, the law gives you the added responsibility of making sure that the equipment is free from defects. The law also imparts to you a duty to select the most appropriate equipment for a particular patient or procedure, to maintain that equipment, and to use equipment properly. If you fail in any of these duties, you could be found liable if a patient is injured.

Nurses on every unit of the hospital should make it a regular practice to inspect equipment for defects or malfunctions. If you notice a piece of equipment that needs repair, fill out an incident report and remove the equipment from the area so someone does not use it.

On November 28, 1990, President George Bush signed into law the Safe Medical Devices Act of 1990. The effective date for this law was November 28, 1991. This law imposed new responsibilities on health care workers, including nurses, concerning patient injuries or device failures that occur within the facility. The law made mandatory that which historically had been voluntary, and increased the regulation of devices through the Federal Food and Drug Administration (FDA). Gathering all of the data requested by this act requires increased coordination and communication between hospital departments and staff.

In summary, the Safe Medical Devices Act requires that reports must be prepared within 10 working days after the facility or its employees become aware of any information that suggests that a medical device was involved in the death, illness, or injury of a patient. (In an earlier device-related law, manufacturers and importers were required to submit reports even though they believed that the incident in question was related to user error, improper equipment service or maintenance, or other "user-related" problems.) Once the report is completed, it is to be forwarded to the manufacturer of the device, or to the FDA if the manufacturer is not known. Significant financial penalties can be imposed upon hospitals who fail to report these device-related incidents. Nursing staff must become aware as to how the procedure is being handled within the organizations in which they work. Since the definition of a device is extremely broad under this act, and includes items that are not

necessarily thought of as "medical devices," nurses should ask that the person or department responsible (generally risk management or biomedical equipment) for reporting provide information describing how their hospital plans to comply. Familiarizing nurses on the unit with the form necessary for compliance will guarantee that the hospital remains in compliance with the law.

Also, make certain that you know how to correctly operate all of the equipment that you may have to use when caring for a patient. But you, alone, are not responsible for patient equipment. The hospital is obligated to furnish you with the equipment that you need to adequately care for your patients. The equipment does not have to be the latest model available on the market; however, it must be able to function properly and must be safe to use.

In *Mather v. Griffin Hospital* (1988), both the hospital and the nurse were found liable of malpractice for failing to have appropriate resuscitative equipment on hand. This case involved an infant who, shortly after birth, began having difficulty breathing. The nurse attending the infant suctioned out the infant's stomach and used positive pressure equipment to force oxygen into the lungs. But, instead of responding, the infant stopped breathing. The doctor present intubated the infant and tried to suction out the infant's lungs. However, the suction tube the nurse handed him was too large for the endotracheal tube opening. With no other way to suction the infant's lungs, the doctor removed the endotracheal tube, suctioned out the infant's lungs, and then reinserted the tube. To make matters worse, once the infant was finally reintubated, the nurse could not separate the face mask from the Ambu-bag® so that the doctor could administer oxygen through the endotracheal tube. The baby became deeply cyanotic, forcing the doctor to simply blow air into the endotracheal tube in an effort to ventilate the infant. After about 10 minutes, the infant began to breathe spontaneously. However, the hypoxia suffered in the interim caused significant brain damage. At trial, the jury found the doctor not liable of malpractice, but found the nurse and the hospital liable and awarded the patient's family $9 million. The court felt that the asphyxia experienced by the infant was worsened because of the nurse's inability to manipulate the Ambu-bag and her failure to provide the properly sized suction tube. It was brought out at trial that it was the nurse's responsibility to make sure that the delivery room was adequately stocked and that the resuscitative equipment was functioning properly.

IMPROPER PATIENT TEACHING

Nurses are responsible for teaching their patients, or their patients' families, about their care and treatment. A patients are being discharged from the hospital earlier than ever before, they need even more detailed information about their illness and how to care for themselves at home. You also need to inform the patient of any potential complications, side effects to watch for, and how urgently medical treatment should be sought if any of those complications occur.

Patient teaching includes both formal teaching—such as when you teach a newly diagnosed diabetic how to give himself insulin injections—and informal teaching—such as when you casually answer a patient's questions or give a patient medical advice over the telephone. Either way, you can be held liable for what you teach, or fail to teach, your patient. In addition, if your hospital serves a large population of non-English-speaking patients, translators should be available to assist in the teaching process. RNs, not LPNs, are primarily responsible for teaching patients. An RN may, however, instruct an LPN to reinforce any teaching that the patient has already received.

Whenever you teach your patient, it is a good idea to give written instructions to reinforce your verbal explanation. Also, always give the patient an opportunity to ask questions and make sure that the patient understands everything. Always be sure to document your teaching in the patient's chart. If the patient refuses to listen to your teaching, or says, "Do not tell me, just tell my spouse," be sure to document that also. That way, there is a written record that you attempted to teach the patient but the patient refused to cooperate.

One of the responsibilities that a nurse has is to teach patients. It is important to follow hospital guidelines and protocols when providing instruction to the patients. In the case of *Roberts v. Sisters of St. Francis Health Services* (1990), a 3-year-old child was seen in the emergency department where a diagnosis of upper respiratory infection was made. The patient was discharged home in the care of her mother. The nurse gave the patient's mother both verbal and written instructions, including a pretyped instruction for fever. Unfortunately, the child's condition later deteriorated a few days later, and the child was brought to another hospital. At the second hospital the child was diagnosed with meningitis from which he did not recover.

The plaintiff brought suit against the first hospital for failure to provide adequate instructions upon discharge from the emergency department. The plaintiff contended that the nurse was negligent for failing to provide written follow-up instructions to see another physician, for the failure to warn the patient to observe for symptoms consistent with the onset of meningitis. In this case, the nurse was not held negligent, because she did give the mother written instructions for fever and other pertinent instructions. The court held that the mother's failure to get additional help for her child was not a result of improper teaching.

Remember, when you teach, teach thoroughly. Also, do not let written instructions replace your verbal explanation. Written patient teaching sheets are helpful, but they should be used only as reinforcement. Discharge instructions should be provided in the language understandable to the patient. It is suggested they be written to the sixth grade reading level. For a non-English speaking patient, use instructions translated into the patient's primary language.

The case of *Niles v. City of San Rafael* (1974) resulted, in part, because of inadequate teaching by the emergency department staff. In this case, the plaintiffs were the parents of an 11-year-old boy. The boy's father took the child to the emergency department after the boy was hit in the head during a fight. The boy exhibited several signs of a head injury, including a headache, pallor, vomiting, irritability, grogginess, and a slowed heart rate. The doctors in the emergency department originally recommended that the boy be admitted. Then, someone in the admitting office incorrectly told the doctors they could not admit the boy because the boy was not being treated by a private doctor with admitting privileges. Based on that information, the doctors told the boy's father to take him home. At discharge, they instructed the father to make sure that he could arouse his son and that the boy's pupils did not dilate. Although the emergency department had a patient teaching sheet available that listed seven symptoms of increased intracranial pressure, no one in the emergency department gave it to the father. Once the boy was at home, the father read a first aid book which listed a slowing pulse rate as a danger sign. When the child's pulse rate slowed even more, and one pupil dilated, the father took the boy back to the hospital. This time, the doctors diagnosed the boy as having intracranial bleeding and rushed him to surgery. The surgeons removed a blood clot and stopped the intracranial bleeding, but not before brain damage had occurred. After remaining in a coma for 46 days, the boy finally awoke; however, he was paralyzed from the neck down and could not speak.

At the trial, the court found that the boy's treatment was delayed because the father relied on the incomplete instructions given by the hospital. Experts felt that it was this delay in treatment that caused the boy's condition to become so severe that brain damage resulted. The court awarded the family $4 million.

LIABILITIES ASSOCIATED WITH THE USE AND DEVELOPMENT OF CLINICAL PATHWAYS

It has been suggested that the availability of written guidelines on the treatment of medical conditions has become a powerful weapon for plaintiffs in malpractice cases. Where plaintiffs once had to rely on hired experts to argue that a procedure was botched, they can now point to official treatment recipes issued by physicians themselves. Although similar statements have been articulated by a number of plaintiffs' attorneys and physicians who are concerned about the impact guidelines will have on medical malpractice, an analysis of the case law does not support these findings.

There has been considerable fear that the establishment of practice guidelines creates new standards of care. It is probably more appropriate to recognize that guidelines should articulate agreed-upon standards of care, but in and of themselves, they do not create those standards. In addition, it must be recognized from the outset that guidelines are meant to systematize the routine care of patients who progress through an illness or hospitalization in a predictable manner. Complicated cases or patients with nonhomogeneous, co-morbid conditions may not be appropriate patients to treat utilizing practice guidelines. Designing a methodology for identifying appropriate ways to identify patients who might benefit from the use of guidelines and for identifying how to handle issues of variance is an important component of guideline development and should not be forgotten.

In the present climate, practice guidelines are being driven by a cluster of similar factors. Quality initiatives stress the reduction of variability as a way of improving outcomes and reducing cost. The forces of managed care are driving practitioners to find ways to reduce the average length of stay for uncomplicated disease groups. Managed care contractors are demanding that attention be paid to performance measures and outcomes. Even the Joint Commission now finds itself looking favorably on the development of practice guidelines.

Given the present proliferation of practice guidelines, the question is how they are being used. Here there is considerable variation. A demonstration project established in the state of Maine permitted physicians to use documentation of compliance as evidence that they have adhered to the relevant standard of care. Most guidelines are used as surrogates for quality, perhaps because performance measures are still quite vague and ambiguous. Still others "talk the quality game" but are really more interested in lowering costs. Nursing care plans often tend to be mandatory and thus arguably also can become standards of care.

The use of practice guidelines is being driven primarily by managed care contractors and providers who believe that their economic survival in the turbulent, competitive market place is dependent on them. It is difficult to identify anyone who is not on the practice guideline bandwagon—if not leading the parade, certainly marching along with it. Depending on the particular guideline, most, if not all members of the health care team may be involved: physicians, nurses, pharmacists, medical technologists, and other ancillary staff. Some clinical service lines, or product lines as they are now called, are developing protocols or pathways that include both inpatient and outpatient care and are

even developing secondary sets of guidelines for patients so that they know what they should expect from their caregivers. This is not surprising, given the pressures to decrease the length of hospital stay for all complicated procedures (e.g., Coronary Artery Bypass Graft) and to increase the patient's and family's involvement.

There were cries that use of clinical pathways would be used against physicians in medical malpractice litigation. Others have indicated that adherence to clinical pathways would protect practitioners from liability. In a sense, both positions are correct. For example, there is little doubt that a poorly designed protocol, with little scientific agreement or credibility, and poor or inconsistent documentation may well lead to liability. However a pathway developed by conforming to the Institute of Medicine's model coupled with appropriate documentation of compliance and/or justification of noncompliance may well strengthen the defendant's case.

There are a number of problems or unanswered questions surrounding the use of protocols. They may or may not decrease costs. Some do and some don't. They have not reached a firm footing with respect to scientific or clinical reliability or consensus. Outcome measurements, though improving, are still in need of additional work. Progress in defining outcomes and in monitoring compliance is often hampered by inadequate clinical information systems; such systems are also extremely costly to install and maintain.

However, despite these imperfections, practice guidelines are being utilized by many health care organizations. Much work remains to be done from an epidemiological standpoint with regard to cause and effect and the use of guidelines. At least one study suggests that decreased length of stay continues even when guidelines are abandoned. As with most other things in life, if practice guidelines are intelligently designed and if compliance is well documented for adherence and nonadherence, then they would seem to be of value to the patient and the practitioners. Poorly designed guidelines with inattention to documentation render them at best worthless and at worst a legal liability. However, the fact that there still is difficulty defining quality in relation to cost does not mean that the search should end.

PRACTICE GUIDELINES AND LEGAL STANDARDS OF CARE

Practice guidelines and legal standards of care are different. A standard of care is the degree of knowledge, skill, and care that would have been exercised by a competent practitioner under circumstances similar to those faced by the defendant physician. Practice guidelines are one of many sources of evidence about what the standard of care should be in any given malpractice case. These sources include the testimony of expert witnesses, medical treatise, and articles in medical and nursing journals.

At the present time, health care professionals believe that practice guidelines should not set mandatory standards of care in malpractice litigation but it should be the case that they are based on existing standards of care. There are too many technical problems that need to be resolved as there is no recognized system for categorizing practice guidelines.

A REVIEW OF RELEVANT CASE LAW

As previously stated, there is significant fear that the use of (or failure to use) practice guidelines will create liability for physicians. A review of malpractice cases does not support this. In *Lowry v. Henry Mayo Newhall Memorial Hospital* (1986), a physician was found not liable despite the fact that he had deviated from a guideline issued by the American Heart Association (AHA). The plaintiff died of a cardiac arrest in the hospital, and the defendant physician had attempted CPR after the cardiac arrest had occurred. The defendant administered Atropine® to the patient as part of CPR. The guideline issued by the AHA called for Epinephrine® to be administered, and the attorney for the plaintiff alleged that the patient's chances of survival would have dramatically increased if the defendant would have administered Epinephrine in compliance with the guideline instead of the Atropine. The court found that there was no medical or scientific evidence that supported the plaintiff's contention and affirmed dismissal of the case.

Although an extensive review of legal precedent was undertaken, only the above case was found. This is probably due to the fact that the use of practice guidelines is a relatively recent phenomena and reported cases—which are only those that reach the appellate stage—have yet to make it through the legal system.

EXAM QUESTIONS

CHAPTER 2
Questions 15–30

15. In general, the courts expect nurses to prevent patient falls by
    - a. identifying patients at risk and taking precautions.
    - b. restraining all patients.
    - c. requiring someone to remain with the patient at all times.
    - d. personally watching the patient.

16. The new HCFA guidelines which address the use of restraints
    - a. seek to provide an absolute standard which can be applied equally to all patients.
    - b. adapt a functional approach which focuses on the function of the restraint for an individual patient.
    - c. mandate the use of restraints for all patients who have a history of falling.
    - d. prohibit the use of restraints for any patient in the Medicare program.

17. The new HCFA guidelines mandate that hospitals or other health care facilities must report to HCFA
    - a. all the names of patients refusing restraint.
    - b. all patients who are restrained for greater than 24 hours.
    - c. any death that occurs while a patient is restrained.
    - d. all education provided to staff pertaining to restraint and seclusion.

18. Ensuring that the rules of right drug, right patient, right time, right dosage, and right route are met is the legal responsibility of
    - a. the patient's doctor.
    - b. the charge nurse.
    - c. the nurse giving the drug.
    - d. the patient.

19. Besides being responsible for the medication a nurse administers, that nurse is also legally responsible for
    - a. the medication handed to a doctor.
    - b. the medication that another nurse on the same shift administers.
    - c. the medication the pharmacist dispenses.
    - d. the medication someone else gives on their behalf.

20. If the pharmacy sends an incorrect medication, and the nurse administers it, who is legally responsible for the patient's injury?
    - a. the nurse
    - b. the pharmacist
    - c. the ordering doctor
    - d. the supervising nurse

21. If a nurse is not sure about a drug order or the dosage of a drug, that nurse should
    - a. call and ask the pharmacist.
    - b. ask other nurses in the area.
    - c. ask the ordering doctor.
    - d. ask an available doctor, not necessarily the ordering doctor.

22. If you ask someone else to give a drug for you because you are not familiar with it, and the patient has an adverse reaction, the court would most likely decide that

    a. the drug manufacturer was liable.

    b. only the person who gave the drug was liable.

    c. that only you were liable.

    d. that you and the person who gave the drug were liable.

23. When a nurse administers an investigational drug, the courts hold that nurse responsible for

    a. ensuring that the hospital protocol has been followed.

    b. ensuring that the patient suffers no side effects.

    c. ensuring that the drug is legitimate.

    d. guaranteeing that the drug is effective.

24. Consider a situation in which you go to the pharmacy, select a drug for a patient, and then give the drug to another nurse to administer. This situation is

    a. illegal, because you would be dispensing a drug.

    b. legal, because this is the same as administering the drug yourself.

    c. illegal, because you would be practicing medicine without a license.

    d. legal, because if the patient needs a drug, you are required to obtain it.

25. Consider a situation in which you are caring for a patient with a newly casted arm. You perform circulatory checks and note that the patient's fingers are cool and slightly cyanotic. You record these observations in the nursing notes, but do not call the doctor. If the patient later sues because of complications resulting from the cast, the court would most likely find you

    a. negligent, for failing to verbally notify the doctor.

    b. not negligent, because you monitored the patient's condition.

    c. not negligent, because you documented the situation in the patient's chart.

    d. negligent, because you did not split the cast.

26. If a doctor appears to be incompetent, you should

    a. ignore the situation, because the doctor is in charge.

    b. question the doctor, but, if he protests, resume your care.

    c. document the situation in the chart and then proceed with your care.

    d. pursue the matter through the hospital chain of command until you get a satisfactory response.

27. Consider a situation in which you notify a doctor of a patient's condition and the response is not appropriate. You document the situation and proceed with your care. Could you be found liable if the patient later sues over an injury resulting from the doctor's care?

    a. No, because once you notify the doctor, your responsibility is relieved.

    b. No, because you documented the situation in the chart.

    c. No, because you are not authorized to diagnose patients.

    d. Yes, because you have a duty to see that the patient gets the care he or she needs.

28. Besides being responsible for selecting the most appropriate equipment for use in patient care, the courts also expect nurses to

    a. make sure the equipment is the least expensive available.

    b. make sure the equipment is functioning properly.

    c. make sure the equipment is sterilized.

    d. make sure the outlets for using the equipment are grounded.

29. The only time you should refuse to follow your hospital's policy is if

    a. it is different from what you were taught in school.

    b. it is more strict than the acceptable standards for the area.

    c. it conflicts with your nurse practice act.

    d. you disagree with the policy.

30. The use of practice guidelines is being driven primarily by

    a. managed care controls and payors.

    b. patients and their families.

    c. plaintiffs attorneys.

    d. health care administrators.

CHAPTER 3

RISKS IN SPECIALTY AREAS

CHAPTER OBJECTIVE

After studying this chapter, the reader will be able to discuss the unique liability risks of nurses who practice in the emergency department, in obstetrics, in the operating room, in mental health, in home health and critical care, and in long term care and skilled nursing facilities.

LEARNING OBJECTIVES

After reading this chapter, the reader will be able to

1. list two legal requirements the emergency department has for evaluating and transferring patients under EMTALA.

2. describe four responsibilities specifically assigned to the nurse who cares for patients in the emergency department.

3. list two primary responsibilities of the nurse working in obstetrics.

4. discuss the court's view on a father's right to be present in the delivery room.

5. identify the most common claim of malpractice relating to operating room nurses.

6. identify the greatest liability encountered by the nurse working in mental health.

7. identify possible areas of liability in the home health care setting and ways to reduce risk.

8. describe the emerging risks associated with working in long term and ambulatory care settings.

If you work in a specialty area—such as the emergency department, obstetrics, operating room, mental health, home health or critical care—you may be performing tasks and assuming responsibilities that are unique to your area. Although the problem areas discussed in the previous chapter will no doubt still apply to you, you may also have an increased risk for liability because of your additional responsibilities.

EMERGENCY DEPARTMENT

Every hospital that has an emergency department and receives money from Medicare for treating patients is required by law to evaluate any patient who comes to its emergency department requesting treatment. The evaluation has two purposes. The first is to make sure that the patient is not in active labor, and the second is to make sure that the patient is not suffering from an emergency medical condition.

Recent changes in the law should be an important component of all Emergency Department staff education. The changes redefined the scope of the emergency room and define terms that in the original law were subject to interpretation.

THE EMERGENCY MEDICAL TREATMENT AND ACTIVE LABOR ACT (EMTALA)

In 1986, Congress passed the Emergency Medical Treatment and Active Labor Act (EMTALA) in response to a widespread hospital practice of transferring poor and often uninsured patients needing emergency care to other facilities. The EMTALA, or the "anti-dumping regulations," applies to all hospitals with emergency departments that participate in the Medicare program. The EMTALA requires the hospital to provide a medical screening sufficient to determine whether the individual has an emergency medical condition, to treat and stabilize the emergency medical condition, or provide a medically appropriate transfer. Recent changes in the law became effective October 2000 and will broaden the term "comes to the emergency department" to mean any patient who presents to a hospital "campus" which can include any property within 250 yards of the hospitals main building.

The expansive definition of "emergency medical condition" under the EMTALA mandates hospitals, emergency department staff, and physicians to expand their clinical view of emergencies and, consequently, treat more patients.

The EMTALA requires a hospital to provide an "appropriate medical screening" examination to any individual presenting at the Emergency Department (E.D.) requesting examination or treatment. The individual who performs the medical screening exam (physician, physician's assistant, nurse or nurse practitioner) should be clearly delineated in the hospital bylaws as having such authority. The purpose of the examination is to determine whether the patient presents in an "emergency medical condition." This condition includes all life-threatening emergencies including acute, undiagnosed pain, pregnancy with contractions present,

and those conditions that might result in some permanent disability or dysfunction of any bodily organ or part if medical care is not rendered very soon.

Additional regulations under the EMTALA, effective since June of 1994, added psychiatric disturbances and symptoms of substance abuse as emergency medical conditions. The medical screening to rule out an emergency medical condition must be provided in the hospital, and patients may not be sent to an Managed Care Plan (MCP) gatekeeper or outside physician to provide the screening. A hospital may not delay providing the required screening or stabilizing treatment, if necessary, in order to inquire as to the individual's method of payment, insurance status or to seek payment approval from an MCP.

In the past, these managed care plans would not reimburse for the medical screening examination if the hospital was not a participating provider. Now, the managed care plans are required to cover the medical screening exam regardless of whether or not the hospital is a participating provider. A hospital may not seek prior authorization for care from an insurer until after a medical screening exam of an emergency patient is complete, and stabilizing treatment has been started. Additionally, when a patient asks about the costs of the emergency treatment, they must be told that the hospital will provide emergency screening and stabilizing treatment, regardless of their ability to pay. But, if a patient decides to leave before a screening exam is completed, a hospital should offer treatment, inform the patient of the benefits of the treatment and of the risks of leaving without treatment, and take reasonable steps to secure a written release. Therefore, E.D. registration procedures are not allowed to delay a medical screening examination and should only obtain basic demographic information necessary to initiate a medical record.

Subject to certain exceptions, any individual determined by the hospital to have an emergency medical condition may not be transferred or discharged until further medical treatment is provided to stabilize the condition. However, if an individual in an emergency medical condition requests transfer in writing after being informed of the hospital's obligation under the EMTALA and is fully informed of the risks of transfer or a physician (or other qualified medical person) certifies that the medical benefits reasonably expected from the transfer outweigh the risks, then a transfer prior to stabilization can be made. However, the EMTALA requires that the transferring hospital "effect an appropriate transfer." At a minimum, appropriate transfer means that the transferring hospital must provide medical treatment within its capacity to minimize the risk of transfer. Second, the receiving facility must have available space and qualified personnel for treatment and have agreed to provide treatment and accept the patient. Third, the transferring hospital must provide to the receiving facility a copy of all medical records related to the emergency condition as well as consent and certification forms. Fourth, the transfer must be affected through qualified personnel and transportation equipment, including the use of necessary and medically appropriate life-support measures during transfer.

The emergency medical condition is considered "stabilized" if there is no reasonable likelihood that the patient's condition might deteriorate from or during transfer, including discharge from the E.D. The definition of stabilizing a pregnant woman with contractions is explicit under the EMTALA. Such a patient is considered unstable until delivery of the baby and placenta.

HOSPITAL POLICY AND SIGNAGE

The EMTALA requires hospitals to adopt and enforce policies to ensure compliance with its directives. Such policies should be frequently reviewed and updated to reflect current regulations under the EMTALA. The EMTALA requires hospitals to conspicuously post a sign in the E.D., in language common to its customers, explaining an individual's right to emergency treatment and whether the hospital participates in the Medicare program. HCFA site investigators, investigating a complaint of an alleged violation under the EMTALA, invariably first inspect the adequacy of hospital policy and signage. Inadequacies of policy or signage taint the remainder of the investigation and may be grounds for independent violation and penalty.

Cases hold that the screening should be sufficient to exclude differential diagnosis that might constitute an emergency medical condition. The nurse must keep in mind that the EMTALA's definition of an "emergency medical condition" is expansive. While the cases to date have not advanced the EMTALA's protection for minor injuries, the possibility of such an interpretation mandates hospitals and care providers to expand their view of emergencies under the EMTALA.

Some care providers and hospital administrators confuse the appropriate medical screening requirement under the EMTALA with malpractice liability. Case law clarifies that the EMTALA is intended not to insure each emergency room patient a correct diagnosis, but rather to insure that each is accorded the same level of treatment regularly provided to patients in similar medical circumstances. Thus, what constitutes an appropriate and proper screening is determined not by reference to particular outcomes, but rather by reference to a hospital's standard screening and treatment procedures. *Gatewood v. W. H. Corporation* (1991).

Instructive on this point is the case of *Baber v. Hospital Corporation of America* (1992). In this case, Ms. Baber presented at the Raleigh General Hospital emergency room complaining of nausea and agitation. She had stopped taking antipsychotic medication and had been drinking heavily. The E.D. doctor examined her and ordered several laboratory tests. Shortly thereafter, Ms. Baber convulsed and fell, striking her head on a table, cutting her scalp. The doctor closed the wound and obtained a blood gas study, but did not order x-rays. The doctor consulted with Ms. Baber's psychiatrist, who believed Ms. Baber's behavior related to her pre-existing psychiatric condition. Therefore, the doctors arranged for a transfer to another hospital where she was directed to the psychiatric department. A few hours later, Ms. Baber suffered a grand mal seizure, and a CAT scan was performed. The CAT scan revealed a fractured skull and a right subdural hematoma, and she expired later that day.

The estate of Ms. Baber sued the doctor and Raleigh General Hospital asserting claims under the EMTALA as well as state law claims for malpractice. The trial court dismissed the claims under the EMTALA, and the case was appealed. At the appellate level, the court concluded Ms. Baber had been provided with an appropriate medical screening. In so ruling, the court concluded that the EMTALA was intended to require the hospital screening process to be unaffected by the ability of a patient to pay, or, at least, to insure that the hospital did not normally provide a lower standard of care to a nonpaying patient. In addition, and more importantly, the court concluded that a hospital must have actual knowledge that a patient is in an emergency medical condition before it can be held liable for violation under the EMTALA. While the hospital or its treating physicians could be found liable under malpractice and negligence theories, they would not be liable under the EMTALA for failure to properly diagnose an emergency medical condition.

As the EMTALA and its interpretive case law are presently constituted, a hospital simply cannot abrogate its responsibility to provide an appropriate medical screening.

The initial assessment of any patient entering an emergency department is usually performed by a triage nurse. This means that you, as the nurse, have a great responsibility to perform this assessment adequately. If you do not, not only could it endanger the patient's health, it could also cause you to be held liable in a medical malpractice lawsuit and cost the hospital a great deal of money. In many lawsuits, the adequacy of the nurse's assessment is the key issue. One such case is *Hollinger v. Children's Memorial Hospital* (1974).

In this suit, a 14-month-old boy was brought to the emergency department by his mother. Earlier, the child's pediatrician had diagnosed the boy as having croup and told the mother to take the child to the emergency department for treatment. According to the mother, when she got to the hospital, a nurse placed her and her child in a bathroom for a steam treatment. The nurse's story was slightly different. According to the nurse, the mother walked into the emergency department and asked directions to the admitting office. After giving her directions, the nurse followed the mother because she thought the child was having difficulty breathing. The nurse convinced the mother to come back to the emergency department for a steam treatment. Then, either right before or right after the nurse put the child in the bathroom, the child stopped breathing and suffered a cardiac arrest. Although the child was resuscitated, he suffered profound brain damage and quadriplegia.

At trial, it was revealed that the child had acute epiglottitis and should have been intubated or had a tracheotomy performed immediately. The lawyer representing the hospital and the nurse argued that the pediatrician was negligent because he had failed to diagnose the condition and had not alerted the hospital that the child was on his way. The court, however, disagreed. It felt that the nurse was negligent for having not recognized the seriousness of the child's condition, and it awarded the child's mother $1 million.

The law also prohibits a hospital from transferring to another hospital a patient who is in active labor or who has an emergency medical condition unless the patient (or the patient's representative) requests the transfer, or the doctor feels that the patient's medical condition could be better treated at another facility. Even so, the hospital must first determine that the other hospital has space available and is willing to accept the patient. It must also arrange for appropriate transportation and furnish the receiving hospital with the patient's medical records.

The nurse's assessment in the emergency room is a key issue in many lawsuits. In *Reynolds v. Swigert* (1984), a 16-month-old child was brought to the emergency room and examined by the nurse. The nurse took the patient's temperature and then obtained the patient's history from the mother. According to the mother of the child, she told the nurse of the child's stiff neck and previous course on antibiotics. The nurse did not perform any type of physical assessment on the patient and in violation of emergency room routines, no vital signs were taken other than the temperature. At trial, the nurse disagreed that the mother had provided her with this information. The doctor diagnosed the child with pneumonia and discharged the patient home with antibiotics.

The next day the patient returned to the emergency room after his condition continued to worsen. At this point the child was diagnosed with spinal meningitis and admitted to the hospital, but later died of the illness.

The patient's family brought a wrongful death suit against the first doctor for failure to diagnose and treat the meningitis. A suit was also brought against the emergency room nurse for her failure to adequately perform a physical assessment and failure to notify the doctor of symptoms suggestive of meningitis. On appeal, the court reversed a summary judgment in favor of the nurse. The court held that a reasonable jury could find the nurse negligent for her failure to perform an adequate history and physical on the child, and for failure to communicate that information to the doctor.

As an example, the case of *Murphy v. Rowland* (1980), occurred because a nurse failed to properly assess and stabilize a patient who had come to the hospital's emergency department. In this instance, the patient, who was eight months pregnant, began experiencing severe abdominal pain. After a nurse mid-wife determined that the patient wasn't in labor, the patient's family took her to a local hospital. There, the nurses examined the patient, talked to a doctor on the phone, and then told the patient's family to take her to another hospital a few blocks away. At that hospital, the nurse and a nurse's aide took the patient's vital signs and checked for contractions and bleeding. The nurse did not call a doctor because, as she later stated, she knew what the doctor would have told her to do. According to later testimony, the hospital was not equipped to perform emergency surgery on pregnant patients. The nurse told the patient's family to take the patient to yet another hospital in a larger town as quickly as possible. The patient's family requested an ambulance, but the nurse discouraged this, saying that the only available ambulance was operated by the funeral home, which had a slow response time. She did, however, offer to arrange a police escort, which the family declined. The family decided to return home instead of going to the other hospital, but the patient died of a ruptured uterus before she got there. The family complained to the Texas Board of Medical Examiners that the nurse at the last hospital didn't adequately evaluate and stabilize the patient and that she also failed to call a doctor. The Board agreed, stating that the nurse had acted unprofessionally and dishonorably. The Board suspended the nurse's license for six months.

A similar situation stimulated the action of *Lunsford v. Board of Nurse Examiners* (1983). In this case, a man, who was driving with a woman companion, began experiencing severe pain in his chest as well as pain and numbness in his left arm. The woman immediately drove to the nearest hospital for help. She left the man in the waiting room and went to find a doctor. The doctor she consulted told her to talk to the nurse. The doctor then told the nurse to send the couple to another hospital 24 miles away. Although the nurse observed the man lying on a table complaining of severe chest and arm pain, and even though she suspected that the pain was cardiac in nature, she instructed the couple to go to the other hospital. The man died five miles away. At the subsequent hearing before the Board of Nurse Examiners, the Board referred to a rule that requires a registered nurse to evaluate a patient and institute appropriate care to stabilize the patient's condition and prevent complications. The Board described the nurse's actions as "unprofessional and likely to injure the public." It suspended her license for one year.

Because you are often the first one to see and evaluate a patient, the patient may give you information that he may not give to the doctor. For this reason, you have a duty to let the doctor know everything that the patient tells you. In the case of *Ramsey v. Physician's Memorial Hospital, Inc.* (1977), the mother of two boys took her sons to the emergency department because they had a head and neck rash and a high fever. The mother told the nurse that she had removed two ticks from one of her sons several days earlier. The nurse did not pass this information along to the doctor. The doctor later said that he had asked the patient about ticks

but received no response. The doctor decided that the boys had measles and sent them home with a prescription for aspirin and instructions that they be kept in a dark room. When the rash spread and the boys' conditions worsened, the mother brought them back to the emergency department. They were then seen by a second physician, who wasn't sure they really had measles. That doctor referred the children to a pediatrician, who discharged them with instructions to report any change. The next day, one of the boys died. Two ticks were then found on the other boy, and he was finally diagnosed as having Rocky Mountain Spotted Fever. After the diagnosis, he received the appropriate treatment and recovered. The trial court originally dismissed the charges against the nurse, but the appeals court stated that the nurse had breached her duty by failing to inform the doctor of the history of ticks. That failure, according to the court, directly contributed to the death of one of the children and the serious illness of the other.

In addition to your assessment responsibilities, you need to also make sure that the patient's record contains all the information pertinent to the patient's condition. According to the Accreditation Manual for Hospitals prepared by the Joint Commission on Accreditation of Healthcare Organizations (JCAHO), a medical record should identify the patient, note the time and means of his arrival, describe the history of the patient's illness or injury, and list physical findings. It should also describe any emergency care given before the patient arrived at the emergency department. Regarding the patient's illness, the record should list the doctor's orders; clinical observations; results of treatment, procedures, and tests; diagnostic impression; and final disposition of the patient along with a description of her condition and discharge instructions.

Cases often hinge on documentation. One such case was *Pharr v. Anderson* (1983), where the nurse relied upon the verbal order of a psychiatrist in discharging a patient. On January 23, 1979, the patient was admitted to the emergency room for treatment of her diabetes and other complaints. Treatment ordered by the admitting physician required the patient to stay a minimum of 12 hours. While in the emergency room, the patient became distressed and uncontrollable. The patient's psychiatrist evaluated the patient in the emergency room and ordered sedation. After being in the emergency room only 1½ hours, the patient stated she wanted to go home. The patient's psychiatrist gave verbal orders indicating that the patient could be discharged as soon as she settled down. Four hours after admission to the emergency room the patient was calm and discharged home but did so prior to the completion of her initial treatments and tests.

The initial treating physician came by to see the patient 30 minutes after the discharge of the patient. After being informed by the nurse that the patient had left, he also gave a verbal order for the discharge, but did not review the patient's chart or treatment. Neither one of these verbal orders were documented in the chart. The patient died later that day from complications of her condition. The psychiatrist later denied that he had given the verbal discharge for the patient.

The family brought charges against the nurse and the hospital. A settlement was reached. Without documentation of the verbal order, there was no evidence that the physician had given the verbal order. Documentation may not have relieved the nurse of all liability, but it would have gone a long way in helping the nurse defend the case.

While you may be aware of your obligation to properly assess the patient, to communicate your findings to the doctor, and to document your findings, you may not be aware of your responsibilities if a patient is transferred from your emergency department to another hospital. According to the courts, once a doctor orders a patient transferred, it is the nurse's responsibility to see that the transfer

occurs promptly. A case where a nurse was held liable for a delayed transfer is *Henry v. Felici* (1988). In this case, the parents of a 3-year-old girl took their daughter to the emergency department after the child had fallen off of a kitchen cabinet and hit her head on a tile floor. After the emergency department doctor realized that the child had a skull fracture, he arranged for the child to be transferred to another hospital that was better equipped to handle the problem. When the child arrived at the second hospital, the admitting doctor suspected that the child had an intracranial hemorrhage. After ordering a CT scan of the brain, he learned that the scanner was not working properly. The doctor felt that the child needed an immediate CT scan and possibly surgery; therefore, he called a neurosurgeon at yet another hospital, who agreed to accept the child. The doctor ordered the transfer at approximately 2:00 p.m. However, because of numerous complications, the transfer did not occur for almost two hours. Once the child was at the third hospital, she underwent a CT scan. By that time, it was 4:45 p.m. The scan revealed a massive head bleed. Although the neurosurgeon performed surgery immediately, the lower half of the child's brain was so damaged that the surgery was not successful. The child died two days later. In the subsequent lawsuit, the court found that the nurse was negligent in failing to transfer the patient promptly and that this delay was the proximate cause of the child's death. Testimony from experts stated that if the child had been transferred when ordered that she probably would have survived. Other testimony revealed that, after a doctor orders a transfer, it becomes the nurse's responsibility to see that the transfer occurs. If the transfer is delayed for some reason, the nurse has a clear responsibility to inform the doctor or hospital administrator so that the necessary actions can be taken.

As an emergency department nurse, you may also be asked to give medical advice over the telephone. If you do give advice, be especially cautious. The case of *Adamski v. Tacoma General Hospital* (1978) evolved after a patient visited the emergency department for an open fracture of a finger. After the wound was cleansed, the fracture set, and the skin sutured, the patient was given instructions to visit his doctor in five or six days to have the sutures removed and to notify his doctor if he noticed any redness, pain, swelling, or excessive fresh blood on the dressing. The next day, the patient called the emergency department complaining of increased pain and swelling. The nurse he talked with told him that pain and swelling weren't uncommon after a fracture. He called again the following day, stating that he was worse and wanted to see a doctor. The nurse again told him that his symptoms were not unusual and that he should see his personal doctor. The patient was finally seen by another doctor, who diagnosed a staphylococcus infection that had invaded the joint. The infection required an admission to the hospital and surgery to cleanse the finger. The court felt that the emergency department was negligent in failing to provide proper follow-up treatment and that the nurses had misled the patient with their advice.

This previous case brings up the issue of your responsibility to give instructions to patients being discharged from the emergency department. When giving instructions, you need to be absolutely sure to tell the patient not only what to do but why to do it. For example, in *LeBlanc v. Northern County Hospital* (1969), a patient had come to the emergency department after being hit in the stomach during a fight. The triage nurse, after examining the patient, decided that the man's injuries weren't critical and that he could wait and see a doctor during regular office hours, which were in four hours. The nurse relayed her opinion to the emergency department doctor, and he agreed to discharge the patient with instructions that he see a doctor in the morning. The patient returned to the emergency department seven days later. He was admitted to the hospital with peritonitis and GI hemorrhage, and he

died the next day. The doctor and the nurse claimed that they were innocent of any wrong doing because the man died solely because he had not consulted a doctor as he had been instructed to do when he first came to the emergency department. However, the court felt that the nurse's assessment that the patient's condition was not an emergency may have misled the patient into thinking that his condition was not serious enough to require treatment. Clearly, the nurse should have emphasized to the patient the importance of his following up with a doctor.

To protect yourself, be sure to perform a thorough assessment on every patient and then document all pertinent information on the hospital record. Relay all information to the doctor, and keep him or her informed of any changes in the patient's condition. Also, if a patient is transferred to another hospital, see to it that the transfer is completed swiftly and safely. If there are any delays, be sure to inform the doctor. And, finally, be especially clear and thorough when giving patients medical advice or discharge instructions.

DEMANDS OF MANAGED CARE PLANS

Managed care has become a way of life for most hospitals and providers of health care. When a hospital becomes a participating provider for a plan, it is allowed to provide medically necessary services as defined in the participating agreement upon pre-approval at agreed upon rates to members of the Managed Care Plan (MCP). The typical provider agreement requires the hospital to obtain preauthorization prior to any hospital visit and/or admission. Some provider agreements required preapproval even for an E.D. visit. Unfortunately, MCP requirements that patients be preauthorized for E.D. visits and/or hospital admissions are unregulated by the EMTALA.

Try as they may, a hospital cannot be a participating provider with all MCPs. Therefore, often a subscriber in an MCP with which the hospital has no contract will present at the hospital E.D. In those circumstances, the MCP will cover only those services it has approved. When the E.D. contacts an MCP, it often denies payment for services provided at a nonparticipating provider and instructs the hospital to send the member to an authorized practitioner or participating provider. In addition, internal hospital financial policies will often require the provider to transfer that patient out of the hospital to her family practitioner or another hospital that is a plan provider. This scenario, which plays out frequently on a daily basis in E.D.s throughout the country places hospitals and care providers in a genuine "catch-22." On one hand, if they choose to comply with the requirements of the EMTALA, they will provide a screening that may violate the demands of the MCP and hospital internal policy resulting in yet another unpaid hospital bill.

In the past, these managed care plans would not reimburse for the medical screening examination if the hospital was not a participating provider. Now, the managed care plans are required to cover the medical screening exam regardless of whether or not the hospital is a participating provider. A hospital may not seek prior authorization for care from an insurer until after a medical screening exam of an emergency patient is complete, and stabilizing treatment has been started. Additionally, when a patient asks about the costs of the emergency treatment, they must be told that the hospital will provide emergency screening and stabilizing treatment, regardless of their ability to pay. But, if a patient decides to leave before a screening exam is completed, a hospital should offer treatment, inform the patient of the benefits of the treatment and of the risks of leaving without treatment, and take reasonable steps to secure a written release. Therefore, E.D. registration procedures are not allowed to delay a medical screening examination and should only obtain basic demographic information necessary to initiate a medical record.

MCPs are not terribly sympathetic with the hospital's dilemma. Although this hospital versus MCP conflict is still rather new, recent case law supports many MCPs' position that this issue is simply a hospital problem. In the case of *Dearmas v. AV-MED* (1993), the plaintiff suffered injury as a result of being transferred to several different hospitals during the course of a few days. The repeated transfers occurred as a result of the MCP's refusal to provide a surgeon to perform the necessary surgery, and it would not pay a non-MCP surgeon to provide the care. The plaintiff claimed that the MCP had violated the EMTALA. However, while factually egregious, the court ruled that MCPs are not subject to the EMTALA.

OBSTETRICS

More malpractice claims are filed in the area of obstetrics than any other area. One reason for this is that everyone expects newborn babies to be perfect; if they're not, especially if they have brain damage, the tendency is to assume that someone was negligent. Also, juries tend to be especially sympathetic toward injured babies and their devastated parents. Because damages are usually based on the plaintiff's life expectancy and the cost of ongoing medical care, the amount of the award tends to be very high.

While most malpractice cases in the area of obstetrics involve the doctor's care, nurses may also be found negligent. When working as an obstetrical nurse, one of your primary responsibilities is to monitor the mother and baby's everchanging condition and to notify the doctor of changes in a timely manner. In *Hiatt v. Groce* (1974), the plaintiffs claimed that the nurse failed to do just that.

In this instance, the patient was admitted to the hospital in labor with her second child. The nurse told the husband to time his wife's contractions and to let her know when the contractions increased. After awhile, the husband asked the nurse to come and check his wife. The nurse did so and then said it would be awhile before his wife delivered because she was only seven centimeters dilated. The husband informed the nurse that his wife had delivered their first child right after she had dilated eight centimeters. The nurse, unimpressed, responded that she was in charge on the floor and that she would call the doctor when she thought it was necessary. An hour later, when his wife's contractions had increased even more, the husband again asked the nurse to check his wife. When she did, she found that his wife had dilated to eight centimeters. Repeating his story that his wife had delivered their first child after being dilated only eight centimeters, the husband asked the nurse—twice—to call the doctor. Instead of responding, the nurse simply returned to the nurses' office. About 10 minutes later, the patient screamed that she was going to have the baby. Her husband rushed to get the nurse, who was reading a magazine. The nurse finally came in, checked the patient, and then rushed out to call the patient's doctor. The nurse then hurried the patient into the delivery room, telling her to "pant like a dog and don't have that kid yet." She then rushed out into the hall where she found a doctor and brought him back with her to the delivery room. Testimony at the trial revealed that the nurse delivered the baby whereas the doctor sutured lacerations caused by the birth. The patient sued, claiming pain, discomfort, and a reduction in sexual activity. The court found the nurse to have been negligent.

Although you are responsible for correctly assessing the patient and relaying pertinent observations to the doctor, you are not responsible for diagnosing problems. The case of *Ewing v. Aubert* (1988) addressed just that issue. This case involved a woman who was admitted to the hospital in labor with her fifth child. At 7:40 a.m. the nurse started an intravenous infusion of Pitocin® to stimulate the patient's contractions. Based on her assessment of the contractions, the nurse increased the dose of Pitocin to 12 drops per minute at 8:00 a.m. At 8:40 a.m. the doctor examined the patient and found that her cervix was dilated two centimeters. By 2:15 p.m. she was dilated eight to nine centimeters, and the nurse encouraged her to push with her contractions. At 3:15 p.m. the doctor was present while the nurse checked the patient's cervix. At 3:45 p.m. the nurse found that the cervix was dilated to the rim. She called the doctor, who told her to order an x-ray to check the size of the pelvis if the situation had not changed by 4:00 p.m. At 3:50 p.m. the nurse noticed that the patient had vomited a small amount and appeared to have stopped breathing for several seconds. She soon became incoherent and combative. The nurse could no longer hear a blood pressure, and the fetal heart tones became imperceptible. The doctor quickly arrived and delivered the baby by Cesarean section. Throughout this process, efforts were being made to resuscitate the patient. Regardless, she died from a massive amniotic fluid embolism caused by a ruptured uterus. The baby also suffered from fetal anoxia. The father filed a lawsuit on behalf of both his child and his wife, claiming that both the doctor and the nurse were negligent. Both the trial and the appeals court, however, dismissed the complaint against the hospital and the nurse. The court stated that, indeed, the nurses should have stopped the Pitocin drip once a diagnosis of arrested labor was made because of cephalopelvic disproportion. However, all of the experts at trial agreed that it was not the nurse's responsibility to diagnose arrest of labor; rather, it is the nurse's responsibility to relate the facts, and it is the physician's responsibility to make the diagnosis.

Although the courts do not expect you to make medical diagnoses, they do expect you to know what to do based on your assessment. Granted, it can be a fine line between making a diagnosis and making a nursing judgment on how to intervene. Consider the case of *Long v. Johnson* (1978), in which the nurses were found negligent for failing to stop a Pitocin infusion during a Cesarean section. As a result of their failure to stop the infusion, the infant suffered severe neurological impairment. In this instance, a woman was admitted to the hospital for the delivery of her fourteenth child. She had delivered all of her other infants vaginally without complications. After she was admitted, the doctor ruptured her amniotic sac. The fluid was clear at that time, but, two hours later, the nurses noted a meconium discharge. The doctor performed an exam, but noted nothing unusual. About an hour later, a Pitocin drip was begun. The mother later testified that, for the next two hours, no one monitored her contractions. The mother then complained of severe pain. Her uterus took the shape of Bandl's ring, which is a pathologic uterine contraction. An hour and 20 minutes later, the infant was delivered by Cesarean section but had hypoxic brain damage. According to the medical record, the Pitocin continued to infuse for 30 minutes after the Cesarean section was begun. At trial, expert witnesses stated that the Pitocin should have been stopped before the surgery was begun. The doctor was found to be free of liability because he had examined the patient every time the nurses contacted him. However, the nurses were found liable because the court felt that the nurses had an independent duty to stop the Pitocin infusion when they observed the Bandl's ring.

Another issue unique to obstetrics involves the rights of the father in the delivery room. While most hospitals and doctors have encouraged fathers to participate in the birth process, the courts still consider their presence a privilege rather than a right. Cases where courts have upheld this viewpoint include *Fitzgerald v. Porter Memorial Hospital* (1976) and *Hulit v. St. Vincent's Hospital*

(1974). In both of these cases, the plaintiffs were groups of people seeking the court's help in forcing the hospitals to allow fathers to be present at the delivery of their children. In the first case, the court stated that it should be up to the particular hospital as to whether fathers were allowed in the delivery room. In the second case, the court empathized with the hospital's decision to prohibit a father's presence in the delivery room. The court stated that the hospital had based its decision on a number of factors, including the increased risk of infection, concern over malpractice suits, inadequate facilities to accommodate the extra people, and lack of privacy for other patients preparing to deliver.

In conclusion, to protect yourself while working in obstetrics, use your best nursing skills to continually assess and monitor your patients. As always, keep the doctor informed of complications, but you should also be prepared to act quickly in the case of an emergency.

OPERATING ROOM

The most common claims of malpractice against nurses who work in the operating room relate to sponges or instruments that have been accidentally left in patients. At one time, under what is called the "captain-of-the-ship" doctrine, the surgeon was liable for such errors. The rationale was that, even though the surgeon was not personally responsible for counting sponges, they were in charge of the operating room and therefore were responsible for any act of negligence committed by someone acting under his direction. However, this has begun to change. Now, courts almost always place the responsibility for instrument and sponge counts on the circulating and scrub nurses. In case after case, when a sponge or instrument has later been found to have remained inside a patient after surgery, the nurse has been charged with being negligent.

One area of frequent litigation for operating room nurses is the leaving of instruments or sponges inside a patient after completion of the surgery. It is the duty of the nurse to count sponges and equipment. When a sponge is left in a patient after surgery, the nurse is often found negligent for failure to obtain an accurate count. In *Truhitte v. French Hospital* (1982), the patient came in for a hysterectomy. Three different counts were conducted—one before, during, and after the surgery. Each time the nurse gave confirmation that the count was correct. Nevertheless a sponge was left in the patient. The sponge was found two years later and was surgically removed. Complications of this second surgery led to a total bowel obstruction, which required yet another surgery. The plaintiff brought suit against the doctor and the hospital for the negligent acts of the nurses in counting the sponges. Both were found negligent as the jury apportioned 55% of the negligence to the hospital and the actions of the nurse. While the nurses are almost always found negligent for failure to complete an accurate count, the issue of whether the surgeon is liable often is left to the jury to decide based on the facts of each individual case.

If you work in the operating room, you may occasionally have a student nurse working under your direction. If so, be aware of what the student is responsible for and what you are responsible for. In the case of *Piper v. Epstein* (1945), a student nurse handed out sponges to the surgeon during an operation, while afterward the supervising nurse counted them. The supervising nurse reported that the count was correct; in fact, though, a sponge had been left inside the patient. The patient eventually died from complications resulting from the retained sponge. In the subsequent lawsuit, the supervising nurse—not the student nurse—was found to have been liable because the supervising nurse is the one who reported that the count was correct.

However, do not assume that the surgeon is never found liable when a sponge is left in a patient after surgery. In *Piehl v. Dallas General Hospital* (1977), a 14-inch laparotomy sponge had been packed around the patient's colon and left there after his surgery for stomach ulcers. After an x-ray revealed the sponge, the doctors had to reoperate to remove it. The patient later sued the hospital, the surgeon, and the circulating and scrub nurses. Although the doctor claimed that he had had no reason to search around inside a patient's abdominal cavity because the nurses had told him that the sponge count was correct, the court disagreed. Although the court recognized that the nurses obviously must have miscounted, it stated that ordinary care would have required the doctor to perform a basic search, which would have revealed a sponge the size of a laparotomy sponge.

As an operating room nurse, you also have responsibility regarding informed consent. It is usually your responsibility to make sure that the consent form has been signed. In addition, you also need to make sure that the surgeon listed on the consent form is the one who actually performed the surgery; otherwise, the patient's rights are being violated. The same thing goes for the procedure listed on the consent form. If the surgeon attempts to perform procedures beyond those listed on the consent form, except in an emergency situation, it is a violation of the patient's right of consent and is considered battery. If you know that this is occurring, then you have an obligation to report the surgeon to the proper authorities. If you do not, the court may later assume you were silent because you and the surgeon conspired together to commit the battery. (Informed consent will be discussed in more detail in Chapter 6.)

MENTAL HEALTH

When working as a mental health nurse, liability may occur when dealing with suicidal patients. Always be sure to follow the doctor's orders regarding suicide precautions. If the doctor feels that the patient doesn't present a suicidal risk, then you will not be held liable for failing to institute suicide precautions if the patient later commits suicide, unless the patient's condition changes following the physician's assessment or the patient speaks or acts in a way that suggests he or she indeed is suicidal. However, you do have a responsibility to continue to monitor the patient. If the patient's behavior suggests suicidal tendencies, then you must relay this information to the doctor immediately. You need to also make sure that any orders regarding suicide precautions, or the lack of them, are written on the hospital record. One case where the orders were not written, and the hospital was held liable for the patient's suicide, was *Abille v. United States* (1980).

In this case, the patient had been receiving treatment for preoccupation with suicidal ideas. When the patient was first admitted to the hospital, the doctor ordered that he be monitored on the most restrictive status, called Sot. It was standard practice for every newly admitted patient to be placed on S-1 status. After several days, the nurses began to treat the patient as if he were on S-2 status. On this status, patients were allowed to leave the unit if they were accompanied by a staff person or another patient. While the patient was away from the unit, he jumped out of a seventh-floor window and died. Right after the patient's death, a nurse changed the patient's restrictive status in the chart from S-1 to S-2. However, the court stated that, because the note was entered after the patient had died, it could not be considered a change in status. The doctor later testified that he must have given a verbal order to change the patient's status, but he said he could not remember it specifically. Even so, the hospital and the nurses were still held responsible for the patient's death.

You also need to observe your patients for any clue that they may harm themselves. If you detect such a sign, you have a responsibility to take steps to protect the patient. In a case in Virginia, a patient

had a history of intentionally burning herself. In fact, over a one-month period, she had attempted to burn herself on three separate occasions. And yet, the staff at a state hospital allowed the patient to keep cigarettes and a lighter in her possession. One day, the patient attempted to set fire to her clothing. Still, the staff did not confiscate her lighter. The next day, the patient left the unit and set her clothing on fire, severely burning herself in the process. The patient later sued the hospital, claiming that she had a constitutional right to safe conditions. The court agreed, saying that the staff exhibited a total lack of professional judgment for failing to protect the patient.

Another aspect of mental health nursing involves how vigorously you can restrain patients and still be within the law. According to *Lake v. Cameron* (1966), a patient's freedom should not be restricted any more than is necessary to protect the patient or others from physical harm. Specific orders regarding the periodic removal of restraints and the need for frequent assessment of the restrained patient should be part of the policy manual and must be strictly adhered to.

And, finally, you need to be aware that in non-emergency situations a patient's guardian may not legally authorize the administration of medications to the patient if the patient does not want to take them. This specific matter was addressed in *in re Roe*. In this situation, the patient was a 21-year-old man who had suffered from paranoid schizophrenia since he was a teenager. Although his father had been appointed as permanent guardian, the Massachusetts Supreme Court determined that the father did not have the authority to consent to the administration of antipsychotic drugs to his son against his son's will. The court felt that it (the court) should be the one to make this decision because it could be impartial.

To sum things up, if you work in mental health, your greatest concern, as always, is the well-being of the patient. This means maintaining suicide precautions when called for, observing the patient for signs that he may harm himself or others and then taking steps to prevent such harm from occurring. Throughout all of your care, though, be sure to allow the patient as much freedom as possible.

CRITICAL CARE

Working in a critical care unit may require you to assume responsibilities for tasks that previously were reserved for doctors. For this reason, you need to be especially careful. First of all, make sure that you have received adequate training to perform the tasks required. Next, make sure that your job description as a critical care nurse includes those tasks as a part of your duty. Your hospital's policy should clearly identify the scope of the critical care nurse's authority.

Also, make sure that you know how to operate all of the equipment used in caring for critically ill patients. This includes not only knowing how to operate the equipment but also knowing how to recognize when a piece of equipment is malfunctioning.

Of course, you are not a critical care nurse just because you know how to operate the equipment. You are a critical care nurse because you have additional skills and are able to make certain decisions. And along with these increased skills come increased responsibilities.

At times, a patient's condition may drastically change and require intervention before you can reach the patient's doctor. How far can you go in treating the patient before the doctor is contacted? The basic rule is that, in an emergency, you can do anything "reasonably calculated" to save the patient's life. This means that you can do anything your background, training, and experience qualifies you to do. As a trained critical care nurse, you should be qualified to perform extensive life-saving measures in the absence of a doctor.

In fact, if you recognize an emergency situation and you do not take action, and it is later revealed that you had the skill to provide the needed services, then you could be prosecuted for misfeasance. Misfeasance is failing to do something that another reasonable and prudent nurse, with similar training, would have done under similar circumstances.

At times, you may be required to leave your patients in the critical care unit to cover an emergency elsewhere in the hospital. If hospital policy requires you to do this, and you have been assigned the task of covering emergencies, then the court probably would not hold you liable for something that occurred to your patients while you were absent. Of course, this does not mean that the hospital would not be found liable, or that the nurse making the assignment would not be found liable. The best course of action would be to make sure that an adequately trained nurse would be available to cover your patients if you should be called away on an emergency.

In conclusion, if you work in a critical care area, it is extremely important for you to keep your skills sharp. Not only are you expected to recognize changes in the patient's condition, you are also expected to be able to respond to those changes.

HOME HEALTH CARE SETTING

Home care is one of the most rapidly expanding sectors of the health care industry. Its growth is forecast to continue as prospective payment forces hospitals to release patients "quicker and sicker," advances in technology enable more complex treatments to be administered at home, and the population ages. As more people require home care and the level of technology necessary to provide that care increases, so does the potential liability for the home care agency and the nurses it employs.

Liability may arise in many areas in the home health care setting, some of them related to areas already discussed in this book but others unique to the home health setting. Liability claims might initially be focused against the home health care agency for failing to appropriately select patients who are good candidates for home care. A careful assessment of the patient's medical record should be completed prior to determining that home health care is appropriate. In addition, the patient's home environment, the patient's ability to participate in the care that is needed or the availability of a family member or friend should also be assessed. Finally, the patient's and family's understanding and expectations of the care to be received should be discussed and agreed upon. An informed consent detailing all aspects of the home health care to be provided should be secured and maintained in the patients home health care record. In addressing the needs of terminal patients receiving home care, a clear understanding of the patient's wishes relative to do not resuscitate (DNR) status should also be understood and documented.

Nurses should then be assigned to the patient who have the skill and training necessary to manage the needs of the specific patient, including the need to perform at a specific level of skill relative to the patient's condition and medical equipment needs.

In the home health care setting, the nurse or other health care worker often finds that they are expected to exhibit a higher degree of autonomy in their practice since they often find themselves in a situation where there is no back up support available. The need to have training in trouble shooting medical equipment and highly sensitive patient assessment is critical. Such training can mean the difference in providing high level clinical and technical support which allows for improvement in the

patients condition or for failure to identify a complication or error which can result in transfer back to an acute care setting or to patient injury or death.

The equipment needs of patients in the home care setting are many and often the equipment is different than what is utilized in the hospital or inpatient setting. Nurses working in home care should expect that their agency instruct them as to the appropriate use of all equipment. Especially important will be the knowledge as to how to trouble shoot malfunctioning equipment and either make necessary repairs or how to have the equipment quickly replaced so as not to cause harm to the patient. Family members as well as the patient should also be provided with education as to how to detect if equipment might be malfunctioning.

Practice guidelines or carefully drafted care plans are also helpful in this area and can assist in helping the nurse define an appropriate plan of care for the patient. Obviously, all orders regarding the plan of care should be written by the patient's physician, but the nurse in this setting is often in the best position to identify subtle changes in the patient which may require a change in the orders originally written. The nurse must be able to contact the physician to secure a change in the plan of care and should carefully document the factors in the assessment precipitating this change and the physicians response to the changes. Communicating these changes to other home health care workers is also vitally important.

Teaching of patients and their families may be one of the home health care nurse's most important functions, for it is often a family member or friend who spends the most time with the patient. Documenting evidence of this teaching and of the patient or family member's response to the teaching should be included as an important component of the home health care record.

AMBULATORY CARE SETTING

As ambulatory surgery centers (ASC) continue to grow in popularity, it is important to examine the liability concerns associated with these settings and to develop protocol which assist the ambulatory care nurse to function in a manner which will maximize patient safety and ensure quality outcomes.

Liability issues for ASC are similar to traditional in-patient surgical settings, as the standards of care are the same. However, differences do exist which require analysis and advanced planning. Specifically, physicians and nurses have significantly less control over patients in an ASC than in hospital settings, both pre and post-operatively. While traditional clinical selection criteria remain key to safe ambulatory practices, because of the lack of control, the need for assessment of patient compliance in the selection process is also important.

Nurses should also receive special training prior to working in this area. Specific to this training is to understand the risks associated with the different types of anesthetic agents utilized in ambulatory care and to have the skills to respond to emergency situations arising from the reaction of the patient to the anesthetic received.

While surgical patient compliance is necessary in all settings, the need for strict compliance is underscored in ambulatory care. This assessment of compliance should begin with the first visit, when educating the patient about the need to remain NPO, the need to have a responsible adult accompany the patient at discharge and the requirement that he/she not drive for a specific amount of time following discharge. If the patient is casual or indifferent about the need to remain NPO, alternate arrangements may need to be considered. Additionally, reasonable conduct requires the nurse to ascertain and document the patient's compliance with pre-op directives, particularly the NPO status on the morning of surgery.

Similarly, if the patient lacks the necessary safe transportation and/or caregiver to facilitate a safe discharge, it may be necessary to consider a more traditional surgical setting, or condition the surgery on the patient's procuring these necessary resources. These compliance issues must be dealt with early on, with patient education and agreement clearly and specifically documented. Moreover, since patients and their families tend to minimize the importance of non-hospital surgical procedures, these concepts should be re-emphasized to the patient during subsequent visits before surgery.

Ideally, ambulatory surgery patients have been repeatedly warned that they may not drive at discharge, and that they must bring a responsible adult to drive them home. Rational people have little difficulty heeding these warnings, and issues arise only rarely. However, it is incumbent upon the facility and nurse discharging the patient to have clear, well considered policies in place regarding what procedures will be followed if an issue does arise. Written policies, comprehensive documentation of all verbal warnings, and evidence of written warnings are excellent tools to frustrate a claim of negligence or to prevent a lawsuit.

LONG TERM CARE SETTING

The long term care setting also presents with a variety of challenges for the practicing nurse. In fact, the long term care setting has seen a rapid rise in malpractice claims and is being watched carefully by the insurance industry. Claims against long term care facilities tend to relate back to three key factors which affect every long term care facility in the country: leadership, staffing and documentation.

Leadership in long term care has the responsibility to see that appropriate staff are hired, trained and maintained to offer residents the type of care that they need. Competition for qualified staff can be fierce in many areas of the country and the need for administrators to locate caring, compassionate staff to perform physically and emotionally demanding work is not easy. The complement of staff must include licensed nurses (registered and licensed practical/vocational nurses) as well as nurse assistants and attendants. Nurses find that they have both the responsibility of performing the tasks which only they can provide by virtue of their state practice acts, but also the challenging task of supervising the care rendered by those hired for support positions. Leadership must be committed to provide the proper training and have rigorous hiring and screening policies to ensure that the work force is properly screened prior to hiring and properly trained once they have joined the staff.

Documentation of all aspects of care is also important in this area. The government has focused in the last few years on the billing which has arisen out of long term care facilities, alleging in many cases that bills were filed even though specific levels of care were not provided. Comprehensive documentation is the only way to insulate the nurse and the facility from these types of claims. Documentation ideally should include: an admission assessment and plan of care, signed informed consent, complete set of vital signs and allergies, resident/family education, fall assessment and reassessment, evidence of advance directive—if one has been signed, and appropriate documentation for transfer or discharge. In addition, documentation is essential to ensure that all activities that are identified in the patient's care plan are carried out. Nurses need to be aware of those entries

which must be signed by them (such as the administration of medication) and which entries they may need to co-sign.

The majority of claims in the long term care setting often arise due to improper staffing. As in many areas of health care, the long term care setting is now seeing patients who have significant medical needs and present the nurse with equally significant challenges. Most of the claims arise when patients fall due to the lack of staff available to assist them in moving from place to place or the lack of oversight when the fall occurs from chairs or beds. Certainly, all long term care facilities should be cognizant of this risk in all of their patients and design falls prevention programs to reduce this risk. All attempts made to safeguard the patient against falling should be noted in the medical record.

According to a 1997 newsletter published by the St. Paul insurance company, a number of long term care claims also arise out of treatment issues. Most significant of these are delayed or omitted treatments, and resident monitoring. Treatment issues arising out of omitted treatment often include the allegation that a patient was not turned as was ordered and thus developed decubitus ulcers. Nurses must be mindful of the types of treatment which are identified in the care plan to prevent skin breakdown. Their charting must demonstrate that this plan of care was followed.

Another treatment area which can result in high cost claims is associated with patients wandering off the unit and either being injured or lost. Patients who are confused or prone to wander must be placed in an area where there is high visibility and documentation must again address how that patient was monitored.

EXAM QUESTIONS

CHAPTER 3

Questions 31–40

31. According to federal law, an emergency department is required to

    a. evaluate each patient who comes to its department seeking treatment.

    b. treat every patient who requests treatment.

    c. evaluate only those patients who have insurance.

    d. treat only a certain number of patients a day.

32. According to the JCAHO, the emergency department nurse is responsible for making sure that

    a. the patient has insurance.

    b. the patient's record contains all information pertinent to the patient's condition.

    c. the patient receives a private room, if requested.

    d. the patient does not have a communicable disease.

33. A primary legal responsibility of a nurse working in obstetrics is to

    a. make sure the patient has no past history of Cesarean section.

    b. ensure that appropriate anesthesia is given.

    c. monitor the patient's condition and notify the doctor in a timely manner.

    d. coach the parents through the childbirth process.

34. According to the courts, if a father wishes to be present in the delivery room, then the hospital

    a. must allow it.

    b. may prohibit it, but only if the father has not taken a prepared childbirth class.

    c. may prohibit it, but only if the father has a contagious illness.

    d. may prohibit it for any reason.

35. The most common liability claim relating to operating room nurses is

    a. lack of informed consent.

    b. sponges or instruments left in patients.

    c. patient misidentification.

    d. improper instrument sterilization.

36. The greatest liability encountered by nurses working in mental health is patient

    a. suicide.

    b. drug overdose.

    c. assault on another patient.

    d. leaving the unit and becoming injured.

37. The standard of care for the nurse managing an emergency in a critical care area is based on that nurse's

    a. willingness to perform the procedure.

    b. assessment that the patient will die without some type of intervention.

    c. background, training and experience.

    d. understanding of critical pathways.

38. In the area of home health care, liability claims might initially be focused against the home health care agency for

    a. failure to appropriately select patients who are good candidates for home care.

    b. inadequate staffing.

    c. failure to determine insurance status of new patients.

    d. improper use of equipment.

39. Liability issues for ambulatory care settings are similar to inpatient surgical settings, the differences that exist are related primarily to

    a. the types of patients typically receiving care.

    b. the heightened use of practice guidelines which seek to minimize liability.

    c. the diminished control over both pre-operative and post-operative patients.

    d. the physician's desire to discharge patients more quickly.

40. Claims against long term care facilities tend to relate to the three key factors of

    a. patients, families and staff.

    b. leadership, staffing and documentation.

    c. equipment, patients and staffing.

    d. use of restraints, improper staffing and lack of informed consent.

CHAPTER 4

DOCUMENTATION: THE BEST WAY TO PROTECT YOURSELF

CHAPTER OBJECTIVE

After studying this chapter, the reader will recognize how to ensure legal protection through correct documentation.

LEARNING OBJECTIVES

After reading this chapter, the reader will be able to

1. identify an advantage and a disadvantage of block charting.

2. describe three common charting terms to avoid to ensure factual documentation.

3. discuss the legal implications of charting tasks completed by someone else or countersigning another staff member's notes.

4. describe a situation in which accurately timed nursing notes are critical, and list two steps for ensuring accurate timing.

5. list three steps for correctly signing off a nursing note.

6. name two qualities that a nursing care plan must have.

7. identify the reason for using only standardized abbreviations.

8. discuss the reason for documenting routine care.

9. describe the correct way to make an addition to nurses' notes.

10. name a situation in which a nurse should never make a correction to documentation.

11. name two purposes for incident reports.

12. describe the legal doctrine referred to as spoilation of evidence.

DOCUMENTATION

The best thing you can do to protect yourself against a medical malpractice claim—besides making certain that you always deliver the appropriate standard of care—is to document your care accurately. You can be sure that, whenever a patient consults an attorney about a possible lawsuit, the nurses' notes are scrutinized for any inkling that negligence occurred. After all, it is the nurses' notes that provide the most detailed account of the patient's day-to-day care and condition. If the nurses' notes suggest that the patient's care was deficient—perhaps because the notes contain unexplained time gaps, show omitted treatments, or just are not legible—then you could find yourself in the midst of a lawsuit. On the other hand, if your notes clearly show that the patient received an appropriate standard of care, then a lawsuit may be averted, or, if you are sued anyway, may help to bolster your defense. Furthermore, since many lawsuits and trials occur long after the injury occurred, your documentation could prove vital in helping you remember the details surrounding your care.

Keep in mind that most malpractice cases focus on one particular point in time. At trial, the nursing records for that time are enlarged to poster size and displayed in front of the judge and jury. Again and again, the plaintiff's attorney will analyze the content of the nursing notes surrounding the time the alleged breach of the standard of care occurred. Could your nursing notes stand up to such a test?

THE PURPOSES OF DOCUMENTATION

The patient's medical record serves a variety of purposes. It is a means of communication between various health care providers with respect to the care they have provided the patient. The medical record also is a business record in that it helps justify to the insurance companies the services rendered to the patient. It is also a legal record in that it is used to evaluate a patient's claim of disability as well as to serve as a foundation for medical malpractice suits.

To make sure that all of these purposes are fulfilled, most states have statutes and regulations that dictate what a medical record should contain. In addition, the Joint Commission on Accreditation of Healthcare Organizations (JCAHO) has its own set of rules as to what constitutes a complete medical record. The JCAHO has stated that each record should properly identify the patient, detail the patient's medical history, and describe the results of a physical examination. In addition, the record should contain all of the doctors' orders on order sheets, observations of the patient's condition (such as through doctors' progress notes and nurses' notes), reports of all procedures and tests per-

formed and their results, and properly executed patient consent forms. Then, once the patient is discharged, the chart must contain a clinical summary describing the course of the patient's treatment and listing all diagnoses. Because most hospitals want to be accredited by the JCAHO, you will find that the patient records for most hospitals around the country contain these basic documents.

Because it directly affects your day-to-day functioning as a nurse, you are probably most familiar with the role of the medical record as a means of communication between various health care providers. After all, most patients are cared for by a myriad of health professionals; these may include numerous nurses, several doctors, respiratory therapists, physical therapists, nutritionists, and social workers. Besides giving all of these professionals a way to communicate with each other, an accurate, up-to-date medical record ensures that the patients will receive care that is appropriate, personalized, and that meets all of their needs. Such a record also serves to educate health care professionals who may care for the patient in the future about the patient's past medical history.

Another role of the medical record that you may not be familiar with is that of a business record. The truth is that insurance companies often refer to the medical record to decide how much money to reimburse the hospital. For example, the insurance company will review the description of the patient's condition in the medical record to determine whether the patient really required five days in the hospital, or if he should have been discharged after three. If the insurance company decides the patient did not need to remain in the hospital for five days, then it may only reimburse the hospital for three days. Also, insurance companies often audit medical records to determine whether the patient's bill reflects the care received. For example, if the patient was billed for the rental of a heating blanket for four days, and the nurses' notes only document the presence of the heating blanket on one day, then the insurance company will deduct the cost for the extra three days from the bill. The patient may have, in fact, used the blanket all four days. But, if it was not documented on the chart, then the insurance company will assume otherwise. you may be aware of the many actions taken recently against health care organizations and providers regarding the payment of significant sums of money. These payments are being made in light of the governments enhanced scrutiny of the Medicare and Medicaid programs and their belief that there has been a pattern of improper billing. A significant portion of the evidence is gained through a careful review of the medical records.

Finally, the medical record is a legal document. It is used to evaluate a patient's claim of disability, such as occurs in a personal injury lawsuit or in a workmen's compensation claim. Often forgotten but equally important to you is the fact that the medical record forms the foundation for medical malpractice lawsuits.

The medical record can be your best friend—or your worst enemy—in the event of a lawsuit. The courts take what you have written literally, and they will use pre-existing documentation to either support or refute your testimony. If the chart documents that the patient received good care, then the courts most likely will believe it. If the charting is sloppy, the courts may believe that the care was sloppy, also. Understandably, you may often be working in short-staffed situations in which you do not feel you have time to chart. However, the courts will not usually let you use that as an excuse. In the eyes of the court, charting is not something you do only when you have time; it's a professional obligation that is part of your job.

TYPES OF CHARTING

Some health care institutions are now using a form of charting where doctors and nurses chart on the same set of notes. The theory is that this form of charting could better facilitate communication between doctors and nurses. This is a legally acceptable means of charting; however, realize that just because the doctor charts a certain observation, that does not relieve you of your responsibility to record your observations under a separate entry.

Some institutions endorse problem-oriented charting, where all health care professionals chart according to the SOAP method. The acronym SOAP combines subjective data (what the patient says about how he feels), objective data (what you observe), assessment data, and your plan for relieving the problem. This, too, is a legitimate form of charting.

One type of charting that leaves something to be desired is block charting. In block charting, the nurse notes in paragraph form everything that happened for an entire eight-hour shift. While this form of charting encourages you to focus on the important aspects of the patient's care, it makes it all too easy to omit important information. This type of charting is also inadequate when describing events that require timing, such as when caring for an unstable patient whose condition is rapidly changing.

Check your hospital's policy and procedure manual to make sure that you're using the charting technique your hospital advocates. Also check the manual to make sure that you know which health professionals are responsible for maintaining which parts of the record.

Nurses should advocate for a record keeping system that does not require that the same information (e.g., vital signs or intakes and outputs) be charted in more than one place in the medical record. Not only is this duplicated charting a poor use of nursing time but it can also lead to incomplete or inconsistent documentation.

RULES FOR GOOD CHARTING

Having nursing records that will stand up in court does not take an extraordinary amount of effort. It just takes thought and attention to a few key rules.

Be Factual

The number one rule for good charting is to be factual. Use your sense of sight, hearing, and smell when you record your observations and steer clear of offering your opinion. For example, if you are caring for a patient who you think is upset, do not just chart, "Patient is upset." That is your opinion. Rather, consider what makes you think the patient is upset. Maybe the patient refused to eat or talk. If so, then chart, "Patient refused lunch. Turned away when spoken to and refused to answer questions." However, if the patient tells you that he is upset, then record what the patient said.

Be careful, also, not to jump to conclusions when you chart. Again, only chart what you yourself saw, heard, or did. Perhaps one of the most common situations in which nurses jump to conclusions is when they chart, "Patient fell out of bed." Unless you actually saw the patient fall out of bed, then you are only assuming that's what happened. Before you put pen to paper, think. What did you see and what did you hear that led you to that conclusion? After some thought, you might chart instead, "Loud noise heard in patient's room. Patient found sitting on floor next to bed. Patient stated, 'I thought I could walk to the bathroom by myself, but I fell.'" As you can see, this notation is definite; anyone reviewing the record at a later date would have few questions about what happened. But anyone reviewing the first note could come to any of a number of conclusions about what happened, including that the nurse was negligent.

Next, avoid making generalizations. One phrase that commonly appears in medical records is, "Patient had a good night." What, exactly, does that mean? What made it a good night? A more accurate note might be, "Patient quietly sleeping. Has made no complaint of pain." Another example of a generalization is the entry, "Taking fluids well." Again, be specific. A better way to record that information might be to chart, "Drank 1200 ml of water between 4 p.m. and 9 p.m." Granted, these phrases are longer and will take a few extra seconds to chart. But think, for a minute, what a field day a plaintiff's attorney could have with the general phrases. How could you explain, in court, perhaps years after the fact, what you had meant by, "Had a good night"? On the other hand, if you chart specifically, your words will speak for themselves.

The same thing goes for terms like "appears" and "seems." Stop using similar phrases and chart what you observe. For example, instead of charting, "Patient appears uncomfortable," chart, "Patient in supine position, clutching siderails. Patient asked, 'How soon can I get another pain shot?'"

Being factual also means that you only record events of which you are personally aware. This means never sign off a medication that another nurse gave, and never chart another person's observations as if they were your own. If another nurse helps you out and changes your patient's dressing, then have that nurse chart the dressing change and chart a description of the wound. If you chart and sign off the procedure yourself, then anyone reading the chart would assume that you were the one who performed the procedure. And, if a complication later develops that's linked to that procedure, you could be held responsible.

Also, if your hospital requires you to chart the work that a nursing assistant performs, then be explicit about whose observations you are recording. If a nursing assistant has bathed the patient, chart, "Bed bath given by nursing assistant Smith." If you simply chart, "Bed bath given," and sign your name, anyone reviewing the record could conclude that you bathed the patient. And, again, if the patient was injured during the bath, then you could be the one held liable.

Also use caution when countersigning another staff member's notes. If your hospital requires you to countersign notes written by an LPN, LVN, or nursing assistant, then check the policy manual carefully. Exactly what, according to policy, is it that you are agreeing to by signing your name? It may be that the policy specifies that you actually watch as the staff member performs the actions charted. If so, then do not sign your name unless you actually witnessed those actions. Other hospitals have a policy that states that, by signing your name, you are warranting that the staff member had the authority to give the care that was charted, and that she was competent to do so. If so, then make sure of that before you sign. The bottom line is, signing your name could make you liable for whatever care was documented in the notes.

Watch the Time

The time that you gave a medication, performed a procedure, or called the patient's doctor could prove a key factor in a medical malpractice lawsuit. This is especially true for emergency situations. As you know, just a few minutes can make all the difference in an emergency. For this reason, you should always make a note of the time for any situation that is out of the ordinary.

As an example, consider a situation in which the patient has just returned from the recovery room after having a craniotomy. Soon after, the patient vomits, becomes agitated, and his blood pressure rises. You make a quick assessment and

feel that the patient may be experiencing increased intracranial pressure. You have someone telephone the doctor while you remain at the bedside, continually monitoring the patient's vital signs and neurological status. You have met the standard of care, right? Maybe so, but if it does not come across that way in the medical record, and the patient later sues, you could be found guilty of negligence. For example, if you recorded the patient's blood pressure at 2:00 p.m. as being 185/95, and the next one you record is at 2:20 p.m. for 210/100, then it looks as if you waited 20 minutes to check the patient. What, the plaintiff's attorney will want to know, were you doing for 20 minutes while the patient's blood pressure climbed sky high? In fact, you may have been taking the blood pressure every three or four minutes. If so, you need to record it. If you do not, a gap of time could result and it could appear that you were failing to observe the patient.

And when you are noting the time for specific actions during an emergency, get the time from only one source. Glancing at your watch one time, using the wall clock another time, and asking someone else for the time on another occasion can play havoc with your records. Various clocks can differ from each other by several minutes. Recording inconsistent times can make your record keeping look sloppy and could also result in a gap in documentation.

But, you may be saying, when you are involved in an emergency situation, the least of your worries is charting. At that moment, you are involved in a hectic battle to save the patient's life. True, the patient's welfare is your first priority. But it is a fact that you may have to later defend your actions in court. To do so, your actions must be documented. Whenever you are too busy caring for a patient to chart, make sure that you jot down key notes, such as pertinent vital signs and times you administered emergency drugs. Then, as soon as you can, transfer that information into the patient's medical record.

Guard Your Name

Always make sure that your notes are legible. This may seem ridiculously petty, but it is not. If the court cannot read your notes, then it may doubt your credibility. Sloppy notes could also make it difficult for someone else caring for your patient to decipher what you did, and this could result in an error. In addition to making sure your notes are legible, you need to sign your name legibly. Sign your name—using your first initial, last name, and title—after each entry in the patient's chart.

When you do sign your name, sign it on the far right side of the column, drawing a line through any blank spaces. If there is not enough room on the same line as your last entry, draw a line through the rest of that line, continuing on to the next line, and sign your name on the far right side. If your notes continue on to another page, be sure to sign off the first page on the last line on the far right side.

If a nurse from the shift before yours has forgotten to sign her name, make some type of notation at the beginning of your notes to clarify where your notes are beginning. For example, you might chart, "Notes for (your name) begin at (date and time)." Then sign your name and proceed with your regular charting.

Drawing lines through any blank spaces discourages anyone from coming along after you and adding information. That is why you should always chart on every line, never leaving a blank space. If you notice that the nurse caring for your patient on the previous shift left blank lines in her charting, then draw a line through those spaces, also.

Use Proper Abbreviations

Next, only use standardized, hospital approved abbreviations. These are abbreviations that you know other health care providers can understand. Using unapproved abbreviations, or using an approved abbreviation incorrectly, can cause some-

one else to misinterpret what you did and the patient could wind up with an injury. Also avoid using abbreviations that have multiple meanings. For example, the abbreviation "bs" could stand for bowel sounds or breath sounds. Consider the possible repercussions if you were to chart "bs absent" instead of "bowel sounds absent" and it later turned out that the patient had suffered a pneumothorax. The patient's attorney could claim that your charting stood for "breath sounds absent" and argue that you did not act appropriately based on that assessment. At that point, it could be difficult to prove otherwise.

Don't Omit Anything

Above all, remember that the court holds the opinion that if it is not recorded in the medical record, then it is as if it did not occur. This means that you should record everything you do—including routine care.

At one time, a standard guideline for charting was to chart only what was significant and not to chart routine care. However, this can be problematic because the alleged absence of routine care can form a basis of a lawsuit. For example, even though it is standard nursing practice to turn a patient every two hours, if you do not chart that you did so, the court may very well conclude that you failed to turn the patient. In fact, it was this exact issue of whether a patient was turned as ordered that triggered the lawsuit of *Hurlock v. Park Lane Medical Center* (1985).

In this case, the patient was admitted to the hospital because of a fractured right femur. The patient was quite debilitated, and the doctor wrote an order to turn the patient every two hours. While hospitalized, the patient developed several decubitus ulcers, some severe enough that the patient's right leg had to be amputated. In the lawsuit, the plaintiff claimed that the nurses failed to turn the patient as had been ordered. In examining the nursing records, the plaintiff found that the nurses had documented turning the patient only 18 times. Based on the length of her hospital stay, the patient should have been turned 117 times.

Expert witnesses testified that, because the nurses had not documented that they had turned the patient every two hours, it was their conclusion that the patient had not indeed been turned. However, the defense attorney was able to get the experts to admit that patient care takes priority over documentation and that nurses can get busy and fail to document everything. Based on the evidence presented, the court stated that the plaintiff had failed to definitely prove that the nurses had been negligent.

This case turned out favorably for the nurses, but it could easily have gone the other way. Most of the time, the court will say, "If it was not charted, then it did not happen."

Good documentation is critical for defending lawsuits against nurses. Even if the care of a patient is meticulous, if observations and interventions are not documented, it will be difficult to convince a jury that such care was done. In *Pirkov-Middaugh v. Gillette Children's Hospital* (1991), a four-year-old child underwent hip surgery and postoperatively developed compartment syndrome. The pressure and swelling associated with the compartment syndrome caused areas of tissue death in the child's right leg. A significant amount of muscle had to be removed from the child's leg resulting in abnormal function of the leg. The plaintiff brought suit for the nurse's failure to monitor, observe, and notify the physicians of the patient's compartment syndrome postoperatively. The nurse's documentation failed to show that the patient's leg was monitored properly and therefore, the nurses and the hospital were found negligent for the injuries suffered by the child.

In *Pommier v. Savoy Memorial Hospital* (1998), the patient underwent surgery for a fractured hip. For the operation, the patient wore anti-embolism stockings, and the operating room staff positioned her with foam padding. After surgery, the patient developed severe pain in the non-operative leg. The patient was diagnosed with left peroneal palsy of the left leg and foot. This nerve damage could occur if there is no or improper padding during the positioning of the patient. According to the hospital's policy and procedure manual, every member of the operating room team had the responsibility to correctly position the patient. At trial, the operating room nurse stated it was her practice to pad all the bony prominences of the knee and ankle during hip surgery. However, on review of the medical record, there was no documentation that the operating room staff had padded the patient's leg. Expert testimony showed that the circulating nurse deviated from the standard of care by only padding the upper body and for failing to document the final position check of the patient in the medical records. Based on the expert testimony and failure of the staff to follow the hospital policy manual, the court found the hospital negligent.

In contrast to the above cases, in *Shepard v. Kinbrough*, the nurse's documentation helped her successfully defend a lawsuit. In this case, a patient was admitted to the hospital with a fractured leg. The leg was placed in a cast, and later the patient developed a blood clot in the leg. The plaintiff brought suit against the nurse for failure to properly monitor the leg. The patient complained that the nurse had not monitored the leg for three hours, failed to observe the changes in the patient's toes, and failed to notify the physician of these changes. The nurse was exonerated from any liability as her documentation showed that hourly checks for sensation, motion, and capillary filling were completed. In this case careful documentation was critical to prove that proper care was delivered, especially in light of the contradicting statements made by the patient. Summary judgment was granted in favor of the nurse.

In *Dumas v. West Jefferson Medical Center* (1998), the patient arrived at the hospital in the early stages of labor at 11:30 p.m. This was the patient's eighth pregnancy. The nurse placed the patient on an external fetal monitor. The patient suffered a late deceleration (a sign of fetal distress) at 12:04 a.m, and the nurse notified the doctor. The patient suffered two more late decelerations at 2:30 and 3:03 a.m., and the nurse notified the doctor. At 3:15, the patient suffered a uterine rupture. The fetus was extruding into the patient's abdominal cavity and fetal heart tones were lost. Upon arrival by the surgeon, the patient received an emergency Cesearean section. The baby suffered brain damage and died seven weeks later.

The patient sued the nurse for negligence arguing that the nurse's performance was below the standard of care. However, at trial the court held that the nurse's actions did not deviate from the standard of care. The labor record reflected the times in which the late decelerations occurred, when the doctor was notified, and the procedures performed by the nurse (repositioning and oxygen) in response to the late decelerations. In addition, the chart reflected that at 3:00 a.m., the surgeon was in route to the hospital, and the nurse had called the surgical team for a Caesarean section and had prepped the patient. The court considered the totality of the circumstances and found that the nurse did not deviate from the standard of care.

One of the responsibilities that a nurse has is to teach patients. It is important to follow hospital guidelines and protocols when providing instruction to the patients. In the case of *Roberts v. Sisters of St. Francis Health Services* (1990), a 3-year-old child was seen in the emergency room with a diagnosis of an upper respiratory infection. The patient was discharged home in the care of her mother. The nurse gave the mother both verbal and written discharge instructions; including a pre-typed instruction for fever. Unfortunately the child's condition deteriorated a few days later, and he was brought to another hospital. At the second hospital the child was diagnosed with meningitis from which he did not recover.

The plaintiff brought suit against the hospital for failure to provide adequate instructions upon discharge from the emergency room. The plaintiff contended that the nurse was negligent for failing to provide written follow-up instructions to see another physician and for failing to warn the patient to observe for symptoms consistent with the onset of meningitis. In this case, the nurse was not held negligent, because she gave the mother written instructions for fever and other pertinent instructions. The court held that the mother's failure to get additional help for her child was not a result of improper teaching.

Maintain Nursing Care Plans

Another aspect of documentation that many nurses are reluctant to do are nursing care plans and discharge plans. You need to realize, though, that the JCAHO, ANA, and various state and regulatory agencies do not consider these plans to be optional. You have a duty to make sure that every patient has an up-to-date care plan. Although some hospitals are not in the habit of doing so, care plans should be maintained as a permanent part of the patient's medical record. Your responsibilities for the care plan include continually reviewing and updating the plan. If you use a standardized plan, then you must personalize it for that particular patient. Always write the care plan in ink. Once the nursing care plan is established, the documentation in the medical record should reflect your compliance with that plan.

Use Flow Sheets and Checklists

Finally, if your hospital uses flowsheets and checklists, use them. These supplemental sheets can save you a great deal of time and can document that you are giving the patient the care she needs. Once you chart something on a flow sheet or checklist, you do not need to repeat that information in the nurses' notes.

Another advantage to these forms of documentation is that nonlicensed personnel can chart on them; they just cannot chart on the nurses' notes. By designing flow sheets with this in mind, nonlicensed personnel can chart the care they give, relieving you of the responsibility.

Keep in mind that flow sheets and checklists are a part of the legal medical record, so make sure the sheets are completed accurately; do not arbitrarily check boxes because someone on the previous shift checked the same boxes. Also, make sure that you document your patient's response to care mentioned on the flow sheet in the nursing notes; the two documents should be used together to give a complete picture of the patient's care.

PRACTICE GUIDELINES: THE PROBLEM OF VARIATIONS

Once practice guidelines are selected and implemented, documenting variations will be important for a number of reasons discussed below. Documenting variations will also assist to overcome the additional hazards in the malpractice area.

Continuous Improvement

Guidelines are not expected to be static. They will change when care givers identify consistently better results based on care that deviates from the guideline at certain points. Those deviations will be recorded as variances. They will be analyzed in trended outcome studies and as alternative steps when the flowchart for a guideline is reviewed and revised.

Exception Tool for Evaluating Guideline

Variances will also suggest the points in a guideline that most often need revision. Exception

charting may disclose strong disagreement by care givers as to the applicability of the selected guideline.

Clinical Comorbidities

Where there are comorbidities not contemplated in the guideline for treating a diagnosed condition, it will be important to show where appropriate treatment of the multiple systems conditions differs from the guideline for one part of the patient's condition. In this circumstance, variances are expected.

Flexibility and Responsiveness to Clinical Condition

A major concern voiced by providers, and a serious impediment to gaining consensus about the content of a specific guideline, is the physician's individual approach to treatment, which has been strongly reinforced at all levels of medical education. The knowledge that variances are an integral part of the development of a guideline acts as an important safety valve for physicians concerned about the seeming mindless approach ushered in by practice guidelines. Documenting variances will act as a bridge for physicians and nurses into a system of guidelines that are recognized to be responsive to each patient's unique course of treatment.

Differentiating Guideline from Standard of Care in Specific Cases

The adoption of practice guidelines for specific conditions may establish a de facto standard of care. While this will work to the care giver's advantage in most cases, it can present unwanted complexity in a case that does not fit neatly inside the parameters of the guidelines. Where treatment has of necessity deviated from the guideline, the documentation of the variance is necessary to show that the standard of care for this patient is different from the guideline.

Malpractice Focal Point

Plaintiff's attorneys can be expected to exploit the tension between the guideline and variance from that guideline. They will likely portray the guideline as the accepted standard, and variances as negligent deviations from the standard. In working up a potential case for suit an attorney, as the starting point for making a malpractice claim, will focus on the variations, particularly ones that differ markedly from the guideline and that are poorly documented.

Dual Charting for Medical Records and Quality Improvement

Historically, medical documentation intended solely to improve the quality of patient care has been kept within Quality Improvement reporting systems. This has the advantage of possible protection from legal discovery, under various state peer review or quality improvement acts. In most organizations, documentation of variances is prepared and disseminated in this manner. The drawback at the time of future litigation will be that material explaining the reasons for deviating from the guideline will not be accessible to the defendant physician in a lawsuit. To remedy this limitation, documentation of variances will need to be charted, in parallel fashion with the Quality Improvement information, or variances can simply be charted as routine medical information in the patient's record.

MAKING CORRECTIONS

No matter how careful you are in your charting, at times you are bound to forget to document something. You may be at home, thinking back over your day, when you suddenly remember something you forgot to report to the nurse on the next shift. You promptly call the hospital to pass the information along. Now, you think, your obligation has been fulfilled and you can relax. But you are wrong.

Simply passing along information verbally does not relieve you of your responsibility to document that information. Before you relax, write out the information that you told the other nurse. Then, when you return to the hospital, add the information to the patient's record.

The way to do this correctly is to find the next available line in the nurses' notes, and insert the current date and time—that is the date and time of when you are adding the addendum. Then chart, "Addendum to nurse's note of (date and time of note that you are amending)." Then chart whatever it is you are adding and sign your name. Never, ever, go back to the original note and try to squeeze in whatever you need to add. That would make a jury question exactly when you added the information, and may make them suspect that you were trying to cover something up. In addition, you should never make any additions to the chart once you are aware that the patient has filed a lawsuit. Again, doing so would only cast doubt upon your actions and make the jury suspect that you were trying to cover something up.

On the other hand, if you discover that a nurse or other caregiver from a previous shift forgot to chart something, call that person and get the correct information. If the information is not critical, then the other nurse can add it to the patient's chart upon returning to the hospital the next day. However, if you feel aspects of your care depend on that information being charted, then chart the information yourself. Then write, "Charted by (your name) for (other nurse's name)." Make sure that the other nurse initials the entry upon returning to work.

If you need to delete something that you wrote, simply draw a single line through the entry and write the word "error." Then initial the correction and insert the date and time. If appropriate, also note the reason for the correction. For example, if you charted the information for one patient on another patient's chart, note "wrong chart." If the reason for the correction is obvious, such as a misspelled word or wrong information, and both the correction and the original entry are legible, then there is no reason to specify why you are making the correction. You should never scratch through an entry so that whatever was written is obliterated. Also, never use correction fluid to cover something. Again, that only arouses the suspicions of a judge and jury as to whether you were trying to hide something. In one case where the nurses' notes contained portions of entries that had been "whited-out" *(Ahrens v. Katz,* 1984), the court allowed x-rays to be taken of the notes to determine what was written underneath the correction fluid. This makes the point that obliterating any part of the medical record immediately sheds doubt on your credibility.

As has already been mentioned, never make a change in the medical record once you become aware that the patient has filed a lawsuit. On occasion though, if a lawsuit has been filed, the hospital's attorney may ask you to review the medical record to refresh your memory. If you do so and you find a charting error, resist the temptation to correct it. After all, the plaintiff's attorney no doubt obtained a copy of the record before the lawsuit was filed—perhaps months before. Instead, make a note to yourself of what the record should have said, and give a copy of the note to the hospital's attorney. You should also know that, in some states, tampering with a medical record is more than unethical—it is against the law. The charges that could be brought against you include fraudulent concealment and obstruction of justice.

Be aware that you do not have the authority to change someone else's notes if you spot an error; if you detect a mistake in another nurse's notes, inform that nurse. Similarly, no one has the authority to change or amend your notes except you. And that includes the doctor.

The case of *Henry v. St. John's Hospital* (1987) involved just this point. In this case, the patient had been admitted to the hospital for induction of labor. After labor was underway, the obstetrician performed a paracervical block by injecting 8 cc of Marcaine® on both sides of the cervix. This occurred at 10:30 a.m. The fetus's heart rate remained strong and steady, and the obstetrician left the hospital. Within 15 minutes, though, the patient was again complaining of pain, and a first-year resident administered a second paracervical block at 11:00 a.m. The nurse documented on the flow sheet that the resident had administered 6 cc of Marcaine on each side of the cervix. Just a few minutes after the second block, the fetal heart rate plummeted. The obstetrician was called back to the hospital, and the patient delivered a baby who was later diagnosed as having cerebral palsy. The plaintiffs filed suit and were awarded $10 million.

The resident was found negligent on several issues, including the facts that a paracervical block was given without consulting the patient's doctor (as was standard practice) and that the block was given at least an hour before it would have been safe to do so. The key point for this discussion, though, is that, after the baby was born, the resident looked back over the nurses' notes and saw that the nurse had documented that 6 cc of Marcaine had been given. The resident then amended the notes to show that a lesser amount had been given. The court found this totally unacceptable. It noted that doctors do not ordinarily write on, or amend, nursing notes. There is no question that the court looked on the altering of the records as an attempt to conceal information, and this only strengthened the plaintiff's case.

You should never tolerate anyone altering your notes. If you are aware of such a situation, report it to your supervisor and document, in the record, that you did so. In addition, do not let anyone pressure you into altering your notes because that person disagrees with what you documented. Consider the above case, for example. What if the resident had gone to the nurse to declare an error in charting the 6 cc of Marcaine and requested to change it on the record? And, what if the nurse had done what had been requested and then, at trial, the plaintiffs were able to prove that, indeed, 6 cc had been administered? The nurse's credibility could have been destroyed and may have been charged with conspiring with the doctor to cover up a mistake.

The only time you should change your notes is if the other person can prove to you that the notes are wrong. To use the above case as an example, if the resident was able to point to the vial of medicine that had been used and show the nurse that only 3 cc were withdrawn, then the nurse might be persuaded. Then, only if the nurse was convinced that that vial was used, and only 3 cc had been withdrawn, the nurse may consider correcting the notes using the procedure already discussed.

DOCUMENTING SPECIAL SITUATIONS

Now you know how to document your routine care correctly, and also how to make corrections appropriately. But what about special situations, such as when a doctor does not respond to your call, or you omit a treatment? Do you need to take special care when you document those situations?

You certainly do. Once again, the key is to be thorough and factual. Always remember that your notes need to be able to stand on their own, without any supplemental explanation from you.

To begin with, let's say that you omit a treatment. It is important that you document that you omitted the treatment, and also give the reason why. Say, for example, that the doctor has written an order for the patient to ambulate three times a day. On one particular day, the patient has been vomiting and, in your nursing opinion, it would be better for the patient to rest quietly in bed than to ambulate. You may be right in omitting the treatment, but, unless you chart the omission and the reason for it, someone reviewing the chart at a later date may think that you simply neglected to follow the doctor's order. An example of appropriate charting for this situation would be, "Patient not ambulated as ordered because patient has vomited three times since 1:00 p.m. Dr. Jones here and aware of patient's condition."

Along the same line, if you deviate from a hospital policy or procedure while caring for a patient, then you should document the deviation and the reason for it. Remember, courts often use hospital policies and procedures to determine the standard of care.

You also need to document whenever you call the doctor to report a change in the patient's condition. Report the time of the call and who made the call (if it was made by someone other than yourself). If you had to leave a message, chart the message was left and with whom, and then chart the exact time the doctor returned the call. When you speak with the doctor, document both the information given to the doctor and the doctor's response.

In situations where you feel there may be some question about what transpired over the phone, it would be a good idea to have a third party witness the conversation and then cosign your note. If the nurse had done so in the following situation, an involvement in the lawsuit of *Hickson v. Martinez* (1985) may have been avoided.

In this case, the nurse evaluated a two-year-old boy whose parents had brought him to the emergency room for what they thought was a cold. Upon evaluation, the nurse noted petechiae, unequal and nonreactive pupils, and that the boy had a fever of 101°F. She immediately had a doctor evaluate the child. This doctor recognized that the child was seriously ill and felt that it would be best if he were evaluated by a pediatrician. The doctor then told the nurse to call one, which she did. While the emergency room doctor was present, the nurse described the boy's symptoms to the pediatrician who initially agreed to see the boy at the office, and then decided to see him at the emergency room of another hospital. Once there, the pediatrician diagnosed the boy as having meningococcemia. He then consulted with another doctor over the telephone, who recommended that the boy be transferred to Children's Medical Center. The boy did not receive any antibiotics until after he arrived at the medical center. By then, it was too late to treat the infection, and he died the next day.

The resultant lawsuit brought out several instances of miscommunication and undocumented telephone conversations. For example, the pediatrician denied talking with the nurse at the first emergency room. Also, although the nurse arranged for the boy's transfer to the second emergency room, there was no documentation to support that action, and no one at the second emergency room was expecting the boy. Finally, the pediatrician also claimed that the consultant had instructed not to give the boy any antibiotics so as not to interfere with diagnosis of the organism causing the boy's illness. This goes against common medical practice, and the consultant later stated, "I do not recall" having said that.

The moral of the story here is that if everyone had accurately documented their telephone conversations, then there would have been far fewer questions about who, if anyone, had been negligent. It certainly would have been a good idea if the nurse at the first emergency room at least had the emergency room doctor listen to the conversation with the pediatrician, or at least cosign the note documenting the conversation. That way, it would be clear that nursing duty was fulfilled.

Many times during the course of your telephone conversations with doctors, they will give you verbal orders. In documenting the content of your telephone conversations with doctors, it is not necessary to duplicate orders that you will note on the order sheet. And, while it is legally acceptable for you to take telephone and verbal orders, you should try to limit the instances to situations in which it is absolutely necessary, such as during an emergency or when the doctor is not available to write the order. This is both for the patient's safety as well as for your legal protection.

When you do accept verbal and phone orders, always repeat the order back to the doctor to make sure you heard the doctor correctly. Note the date and time of the order, and, below the order, write t.o. for telephone order, or v.o. for verbal order. Write the doctor's name and then sign your name. Make sure that the doctor countersigns the order as soon as possible. Actually, every hospital has a policy regarding the time limit for countersigning verbal orders, so check your hospital's policy manual. If the doctor fails to countersign an order, and the patient later sues, the doctor could deny having given the order and you could be accused of practicing medicine without a license.

When you transcribe orders, make a check mark, in ink, by each item as you take it off. When you have reached the end of the list of orders, draw a single line through any blank spaces between the last order and the doctor's signature. This will prevent anyone from going back later and inserting another order. Next, sign your name under the doctor's signature, and insert the date and time.

What if the doctor writes an order for something with which you disagree? Of course, if the order could have life-threatening results, you would first discuss it with the doctor and then, if necessary, talk with your supervisor or other persons in authority. But, if the situation would not produce life-threatening results, you can protect yourself by simply documenting the situation. Consider, for example, a situation in which the doctor orders a patient's I.V. fluids to be discontinued. You disagree with this decision, because the patient has been vomiting repeatedly and has not been consuming what you think is an adequate amount of liquids. First, you would talk to the doctor to make him aware of the situation. If he still wants the I.V. fluids discontinued, then you should chart, "I.V. discontinued per order Dr. Smith. Dr. Smith informed that patient vomited 4 times in past 3 hours and that patient's intake has been 150 ml for past 8 hours." You would then, of course, continue to monitor the patient closely and notify the doctor as necessary.

Finally, your discharge summary is another piece of charting that is important. First of all, patients are being discharged earlier and earlier from the hospital. This means that the patient's condition at discharge—along with what was taught about home and follow-up care could be a matter for investigation at a later date. Therefore, your note should be thorough. To make sure that your summary is complete, check your hospital's policy manual for specific guidelines. Basically, you should describe the patient's condition at discharge, specify who the escort is, and note the mode of transportation. You should also document any patient teaching, including diagnosis, medications, activity, diet, follow-up care, referrals, and any special procedures that need to be done. If you gave the patient a copy of a home-care instruction sheet, mention that also. If the patient demonstrates comprehension of your instructions—such as return demonstration with insulin or performing some other procedure—then document that, also.

Contributory Negligence

One area that you may not be aware that you need to watch for, much less document, are any actions of the patient that may hinder expected medical progress. For example, consider that you are caring for a post-operative laminectomy patient. The doctor has written an order for the patient to wear a special corset to support his back

whenever he is out of bed. However, despite repeated instructions by you, you have found the patient out of bed on several occasions without his corset. This is very significant and could mean the difference between winning and losing a malpractice lawsuit. Suppose that the patient later develops complications and sues. If you have carefully documented your instructions to the patient and also the instances in which he defied your instructions, then the defense attorney could possibly show that the patient's own actions caused, or at least contributed to, his complications. This aspect of the law is known as contributory negligence.

However, it is often difficult to successfully claim contributory negligence in a medical malpractice case. This is because the court generally feels that health care providers bear the greatest responsibility for the patient's welfare while hospitalized; after all, health care professionals usually know more about the patient's condition than the patient does. However, if you carefully document when you instruct the patient on a particular topic, and then also document that the patient demonstrated an understanding for the teaching, then you will be laying a good foundation for the argument that the patient contributed to an injury if he later acts contrary to your teaching and becomes injured.

An example of a case in which the hospital successfully argued that the patient was negligent and caused her injury is *Seymour v. Victory Memorial Hospital* (1978). The patient in this instance was hospitalized and receiving sedatives because of a back injury. The nurses told the patient, who was a heavy smoker, not to smoke unless someone was with her to make sure that she did not fall asleep while smoking. The nurses took the patient's cigarettes and lighter and told her to call whenever she wanted to smoke. After making 15 to 20 calls to the nurses' station a day, the patient bought some cigarettes from a volunteer cart. She began to smoke without anyone present and, in the process, dropped a match and burned herself. She sued the hospital, but the court stated that the hospital was not liable. The court pointed out that the patient knew the procedure to use when she wanted to smoke and that she was aware of the danger if she did not follow the procedure.

On the other hand, this type of an argument will not hold if the patient is confused, disoriented, or suffers from some condition that may hinder the ability to understand your instructions (such as extreme pain or hypoxia). For example, in *Kent v. County of Hudson* (1968), a 65-year-old senile man was admitted to the hospital. The patient's family told the nurses that the man had caused fires in the past while smoking. So, the nurses took the patient's cigarettes away and told him not to smoke unless someone was with him. They also asked the patient's family to make sure that someone stayed with the patient whenever he smoked. Despite these precautions, the nurses later found the patient on fire and he later died. The patient's family sued. At trial, the court told the defense attorneys that they did not have enough evidence to support a claim of contributory negligence. As a result, the jury found both the hospital and the nurses liable for the patient's injuries.

So, in addition to taking every precaution to ensure the patient's safety, thoroughly document your actions and those of the patient.

INCIDENT REPORTS

Despite the best precautions, sometimes accidents occur; and, as you probably know, any occurrence that is outside the hospital's usual routine needs to be documented by an incident report. Reportable incidents include injury to a patient, visitor, or employee; medication errors; and patient complaints.

A main purpose of incident reports is simply to allow the hospital administration to identify problem areas within the hospital system and institute corrective action. For example, if several incident reports are filed regarding patient falls in a certain unit of the hospital, hospital administrators may decide to investigate. They may then discover that several of the bathrooms on that unit do not have grab bars. As a result, they may install grab bars and help prevent patient falls in the future.

Another purpose behind incident reports is to alert the hospital administration and the hospital's insurance company of an event that may result in a lawsuit. If an incident is serious enough, they may investigate. But even if they do not investigate at that time, and a lawsuit is filed in the future, the incident report will still provide valuable information, including a description of the incident and a list of witnesses.

Some nurses may try to avoid filling out incident reports unless a doctor or a supervisor orders them to complete one. However, this is not the correct attitude to have. Completing incident reports will assist the hospital staff to identify problematic situations and correct them prior to other similar incidents occurring. Including the names of all staff involved (including witnesses) will allow for a thorough investigation and initiation of appropriate corrective action. Creating a safe environment for patients should be the goal of every employee in the hospital.

Whenever you complete an incident report, keep your statements factual and objective. Describe what happened as best you can, confining yourself to whatever you yourself witnessed, not what someone else told you happened. Just as in charting, do not include your opinions or make generalizations. Also do not draw any conclusions about what caused the incident, and do not state who you feel was at fault or how you feel the incident could be avoided in the future.

Besides describing the incident on the report, you need to also describe it in your nurses' notes. Again, follow the general guidelines for charting and describe the incident as factually as possible. However, when you chart, do not mention that an incident report was filed. Also, do not place a copy of the incident report in the file. Incident reports are an administrative tool and do not contain clinical information pertinent to the patient's care. Mentioning an incident report would only serve as a red flag to an attorney if the patient later filed a lawsuit. It might also make the attorney wonder what else happened that was mentioned in the incident report and not in the chart.

Whether the plaintiff's attorney can actually obtain a copy of the incident report varies from state to state. Most courts take the view that incident reports are a form of internal communication and part of the quality improvement process and, therefore, are not available for review by outsiders. However, some courts do allow incident reports to be introduced into evidence during a malpractice lawsuit. For this reason, it is even more important that you keep to the facts and steer clear of generalizations and conclusions when describing the incident.

While some nurses dread having to fill out an incident report, rest assured that it is unlikely that the report will be used against you (unless, of course, you repeatedly make the same mistakes). Remember, the main purpose of the report is to alert the hospital administrators to the fact that the incident happened. It is up to them whether to investigate in anticipation of a lawsuit, or to make some type of change to prevent the mistake from occurring again.

What should you tell your patient following an incident? First of all, answer questions as honestly as you can. Do not try to explain why the incident happened, and do not blame anyone. If you were not personally involved, refer the patient to whoever can answer his questions. The most important thing, though, is to maintain rapport and be honest. Do not try to cover something up,

and do not make excuses. That may only serve to make the patient more suspicious.

If the thought of talking to the patient about the incident makes you extremely nervous, ask your supervisor, hospital risk manager, or an administrator to talk to the patient, instead. Also, do not hesitate to ask your supervisor how you should respond to the patient's questions.

NEW DOCTRINE RELATED TO SPOILATION OF EVIDENCE

Medical malpractice cases or the threat of such cases against nurses, physicians, or hospitals can have devastating effects on both the institution and providers. Often, when questions about care arise, the medical record provides for the hospital and caregiver the best evidence to support that appropriate care was indeed provided. Nurses are very familiar with basic tenets of documentation and with prohibitions against alteration of the medical record. Recently, however, a new concern has been addressed by the courts that poses an additional burden on nurses, medical records departments, and the hospital in general.

For purposes of recent court discussion, the medical record includes all standard forms determined by the institution to be part of the complete record, including history and physical, progress notes, nurses' notes, laboratory and radiology reports, and special care unit flow-sheets. In addition, items such as fetal monitoring strips, EKG tracings and X-ray films, MRI and CT scans are also part of the medical record and must be treated with the same care as those other items typically referred to as the patient's chart.

In recent cases, courts determined that when information is not available at the time of discovery and trial, it will be presumed to have been lost for a reason—that reason being the destruction of detrimental evidence. When this occurs, the hospital can be assessed for punitive damages and can have the burden of proving that the information—if it had been available—would not have supported the allegations of the plaintiff.

Spoilation of Medical Record Case

In *Rodgers v. St. Mary's Hospital of Decatur* (1998), the Illinois Appellate Court held that the violation of a statute designed for the protection of human life or property is prima facie evidence of negligence. In this case, the court held that the plaintiff was entitled to a second cause of action against the defendant hospital due to the hospital's failure to retain x-rays pursuant to a state statute. The court referred to this loss of x-rays as spoilation of medical evidence and stated that, absent evidence to the contrary, the jury could presume that the x-rays had been purposely lost to hide information that would have been damaging to the hospital's case.

Nurses need to be particularly aware of the supplemental documents that often accompany the care of a patient during cardiac arrest and transport. They also need to be advised of the fact that the more information they are required to document on multiple sheets (for example, flow sheets, graphic records, Intake & Output sheets) the more likely that some information will be lost or not documented, giving rise to potential claims of evidence spoilation.

COMPUTER DOCUMENTATION

Some hospitals are now using computer documentation in an effort to break out from under the mountain of paperwork associated with keeping records on every patient. To use the system, a nurse simply types in an assigned code and follows that with the patient's code number. The patient's record will then appear on a monitor, which looks like a small television screen, on the nursing unit. The nurse then has an option of printing out all or part of the patient's record.

Computer documentation has obvious advantages. First, it saves both time and phone calls when you want to find out the results of laboratory tests. Instead of the result coming to the unit on a lab slip, the technician will insert the value directly into the computer, making it immediately available for your review. Next, computers help standardize charting by offering you variables from which to choose for each body system. For example, when observing the patient's skin, the computer will give you options from which to choose, such as pale, cyanotic, flushed, dry, diaphoretic, and so on.

But the system is not without its flaws. Some of the problems with the system include the fact that computers can break down, making information unavailable. Worse, they have been known to scramble information. There are also questions of legality and confidentiality that should be considered. New federal regulations, known as HIPAA legislation (Health Insurance Portability and Accountability Act), are currently being drafted and is likely to use it in dramatic changes in this area.

The JCAHO has informally authorized the use of computer documentation as a substitute for manual record keeping. However, computers will not be accepted everywhere without some debate.

The main complaint is that it could be difficult to insure the patient's privacy once all medical information has been inserted into a computer. For starters, the patient's record would no longer be protected under the watchful eye of the unit secretary. Rather, any one of a number of monitors located throughout the hospital could be used to call up the patient's record. Even requiring the use of special access codes cannot guarantee that an unauthorized person will not be able to access the patient's record.

When using a computer to document your patient care, follow the same rules as you would for documenting manually. In addition, guard your computer access number and do not let anyone else use it. If you suspect that someone has used your number, then let your supervisor know.

All in all, many experts feel that computer documentation is the way of the future and that it can help free you from an endless parade of paperwork so that you can devote more time to your patients.

CONCLUSION

As you can see, both what and how you chart can have great legal implications. Besides making a difference in whether you win or lose a malpractice lawsuit, it can also affect whether the patient's insurance company adequately compensates the hospital for care the patient has received, or whether the patient receives adequate compensation for an injury suffered while at work.

In addition to your responsibility to accurately document the patient's care, you are also held responsible for being aware of everything that is recorded in the patient's chart. This means that, whenever you begin to care for a patient, you should take a few minutes to review the patient's medical record. Even if the nurse taking care of the patient on the previous shift does not give you certain information in her verbal report, if that information is contained in the chart, then the court will hold you responsible for being aware of it. Granted, this is one more demand on your time; but, for the patient's welfare, and your protection, it is imperative that you take the time you need to read the patient's chart.

EXAM QUESTIONS

CHAPTER 4
Questions 41–53

41. The main problem with block charting, where a nurse records in paragraph form everything that happened in a routine shift, is that it is

    a. time-consuming.

    b. too lengthy.

    c. illegal.

    d. inadequate for documenting care that requires timing.

42. A main rule to remember when charting is to

    a. give your opinion.

    b. be factual.

    c. use generalizations.

    d. draw conclusions.

43. Of the charting samples below, which is the most factual?

    a. patient had a good night

    b. patient appears comfortable

    c. patient eating well

    d. patient drank 1200 ml of water between 4 p.m. and 9 p.m

44. When countersigning notes written by an LPN, LVN, or a nursing assistant, you should first

    a. make sure the person who completed the work is the person writing the note.

    b. make sure that you personally know the person writing the note.

    c. check the hospital's policy manual to see what you're warranting.

    d. make sure that the work performed was satisfactory.

45. To ensure accurate timing of your notes, you should

    a. always get the time from the same source.

    b. get the time from the nearest source.

    c. estimate the time to the best of your ability.

    d. always get the time from another person to ensure objectivity.

46. The proper way to sign off your nursing notes is to

    a. sign your first initial, last name, and title after each entry.

    b. sign your full name after the first entry and simply use your initials on subsequent entries.

    c. sign your full name only when noting medications administered or important procedures performed.

    d. sign your name once, at the end of your shift.

47. If a nurse from a previous shift has forgotten to sign the nursing notes, you should

    a. sign it for the nurse.

    b. draw a line through the space where a signature should have been and then begin your charting.

    c. use a different color ink to differentiate your charting from others.

    d. make a notation at the beginning of your notes to clarify where your notes begin.

48. The rule to remember when using abbreviations is to

    a. use as many abbreviations as possible to save time and space.

    b. use no abbreviations at all.

    c. use abbreviations only on flow sheets but never in nursing notes.

    d. use only standard abbreviations.

49. The reason you should always document routine care is

    a. the court holds the opinion that if it was not charted, then it was not done.

    b. so that nurses on the next shift will know the patient has been bathed.

    c. to placate the patient's family.

    d. to substantiate to nursing service how you spent your shift.

50. When should you never make a correction in your nursing notes?

    a. after the patient has been discharged

    b. if the patient dies

    c. if more than 24 hours have elapsed since the time the note was first written

    d. once a lawsuit has been filed

51. Who has the authority to change the notes of a nurse?

    a. only the nurse who wrote the note

    b. any nurse, as long as that nurse has comparable training

    c. the doctor of the patient the note concerns

    d. any doctor

52. A main purpose of incident reports is

    a. to allow hospital administration to identify problem areas.

    b. to identify bad nurses.

    c. to discipline the person responsible for the incident.

    d. to cover up any wrongdoing.

53. Under the doctrine of spoliation of evidence information about the patient which is not available at the time of discovery or trial will be presumed to have been lost because

    a. the hospital had a poor medical records department.

    b. the evidence the record contained was detrimental to the hospital or provider.

    c. the information in the record was not important or necessary.

    d. the information was confidential and the hospital was seeking to protect the patient.

CHAPTER 5

YOUR RESPONSIBILITIES
AS AN EMPLOYEE

CHAPTER OBJECTIVE

After studying this chapter, the reader will be able to describe the legal implications of making work assignments, working in an understaffed situation, refusing a work assignment, floating, and mandatory overtime.

LEARNING OBJECTIVES

After reading this chapter, the reader will be able to

1. describe two actions a nurse can legally take when making an assignment in an understaffed situation to help ensure that the patient receives adequate care.

2. discuss the legal implications of assigning tasks to someone who is not authorized to perform them.

3. identify three options for intervention when a charge nurse realizes that a staff nurse is delivering inadequate care.

4. describe the JCAHO's position regarding what constitutes adequate staffing.

5. specify how the legal implications of understaffing varies depending upon whether the situation is acute or chronic.

6. list two responsibilities of the charge nurse on an understaffed shift.

7. identify one situation in which a nurse should always refuse an assignment.

8. identify two reasons a court may rule against a nurse who refuses to float.

9. describe the protection offered by law to a nurse who works to improve the conditions of their place of employment.

Now that you understand your legal responsibilities when administering direct patient care, you need to learn your obligations as an employee of a hospital or other health care institution. For example, many nurses make work assignments on a daily basis, but few realize the responsibilities that the law thrusts upon them when they do so. Also, what about short-staffing situations, hospital policies that require floating, and your desire to refuse a work assignment? Do you know how to handle each of these situations while protecting your rights and fulfilling your responsibilities?

MAKING WORK ASSIGNMENTS

Whenever you make a work assignment, you are assuming additional legal responsibilities. The law holds you accountable for making the assignments properly so that all of the patients' needs will be met. If an assignment is inappropriate, and a patient is harmed, you could be held accountable.

The Joint Commission on Accreditation of Healthcare Organizations (JCAHO) has set down certain requirements with regard to making work assignments. To satisfy these requirements, your first step in making an assignment would be to evaluate the physical condition of each patient. How intensive are the patient's needs? Does the patient's medical regimen include procedures for which certain skills are required? Does the patient have an infection that would require an adjustment in nursing assignment to prevent accidental cross contamination? Next, you need to consider the patient's psychological and emotional needs. Does the patient have exceptional needs in either of these areas that require consideration? Also, do not overlook the patient's needs for teaching and discharge planning. While it can be tempting to decide that these activities do not have immediate significance, the law disagrees. Patient teaching and discharge planning are very real, very pertinent aspects of the patient's care.

Once you have carefully evaluated the patient, you must then evaluate the staff you have available. Who has the educational background and experience necessary to care for each patient? When assigning a staff member to a patient, you must believe that that person is competent to adequately care for that patient. Knowingly assigning someone whom you know to be deficient in certain skills to care for a patient who has needs in those areas would be negligent on your part. For example, imagine that you have just admitted a patient to your unit who requires peritoneal dialysis. The most available staff member is a nurse who recently mismanaged another patient on peritoneal dialysis. On that occasion, the nurse infused the wrong type and wrong amount of dialysate and was inconsistent in monitoring the dwell times. For you to go ahead and assign this nurse to the new admission without taking any steps to ensure the

patient's safety could make you liable if an injury resulted. If no other nurse is available, you may have to assign this nurse to the patient—just make sure that someone else more qualified either performs the procedure or closely supervises the first nurse.

Also, make sure that you do not assign tasks to someone who is not authorized to perform them. This includes LPNs, private duty nurses, and agency nurses. For example, if the state or your hospital prohibits LPNs from removing sutures, and you instruct an LPN to remove a patient's sutures, then you could be found liable if the patient is injured in the process.

Unfortunately, in many clinical situations, you may be faced with too many patients and too few staff members. When this occurs, you can legally decide which routine tasks are not absolutely necessary and instruct your staff to omit them. Of course, when you take this step, you need to make absolutely certain that deleting such care will not harm the patient.

For example, you can probably safely omit a patient's evening back rub, but omitting every two-hour turning in a debilitated patient could have medical repercussions for which you could be held accountable. In the eyes of the court, inadequate staffing is no excuse for inadequate care.

Also, when making an assignment in a short-staffed situation, consider which other professionals might be available to relieve some of your staff's burden. Knowing how to appropriately delegate patient care is an important responsibility of the nurse manager. For example, perhaps the respiratory therapy department is better staffed and can assume responsibility for chest percussion and postural drainage treatments. Also, maybe I.V. therapy can give all the I.V. drugs for that shift. Other personnel that may be able to assume additional responsibilities include clinical nurse specialists, pharmacists, laboratory technicians, and interns. Knowing that some of these professionals would be able to assume some of the responsibilities involved in caring for the patients on your unit could make a difference in how you assign your staff.

Once you have completed the assignment, your responsibilities are not over. The law expects you to adequately supervise your staff. As a charge nurse, this means assisting other nurses as needed and periodically checking to make sure that the patient is receiving adequate care. Through your supervision, if you learn that a nurse is not delivering the appropriate standard of care, you must step in at once. Actions you can take include helping the nurse yourself, assigning another staff member to help the nurse, or rearranging the assignment. Always remember that your first responsibility is to the patient. If you ever become aware of another staff member's incompetence—and this includes agency nurses and private duty nurses—you must first intervene directly to protect the patient, and then you must report the situation to your supervisor.

A supervisory nurse's responsibility is broader than just supervising staff. For example, the law considers supervision to include providing adequate policies and procedures, orientation, inservice education programs, and performance evaluations.

Although making an assignment is a significant responsibility, rest assured that you will not automatically be held liable if one of the nurses to whom you have assigned patients commits malpractice. After all, each nurse is accountable for his or her own actions. You could be held liable, though, if you failed in some way to assign the nurse appropriately.

The key to protecting yourself is to make sure that you use all of the information available—about both the patients and the available staff—to appropriately delegate the duties of patient care.

THE PROBLEM OF UNDERSTAFFING

Making an ideal assignment depends on having adequate staff available. Unfortunately, this is often not the case. Understaffing is a very real, and often chronic, problem at many health care facilities. And, in light of the financial difficulties facing many hospitals today and the shortage of nurses in many areas, the problem is not likely to disappear any time soon.

It is becoming more common for lawsuits to specifically accuse hospitals of negligence for failing to have adequate staff to meet patients' needs. One such case is *Leavitt v. St. Tampmany Parish Hospital* (1981). In this case, the patient was a 57-year-old woman who had been admitted to the hospital because of congestive heart failure and diabetes. The patient was weak and was also taking drugs that impaired her thinking.

The nurses were aware of this, so they told the patient to call someone whenever she needed to get out of bed. At one point, the patient put on the call light to ask for help to go to the bathroom. The patient later stated that she waited for 15 minutes, but that no one ever came. As a result, the patient got out of bed herself, went to the bathroom, and fell as she tried to climb back into bed. She sued the hospital, and the court agreed that the hospital had breached its duty to the patient by having less-than-adequate staff available. The court stated that the patient had a right to expect someone to respond promptly to her call light.

However, it is difficult to specify exactly how many employees a hospital should have in order to provide adequate staffing. Instead of providing specific nurse-patient ratios that are acceptable, the law and regulatory agencies overseeing health care state that a hospital must have enough care providers on duty at all times to give patients the specialized care they need. The JCAHO also says that staffing must be sufficient "to assure prompt recognition of any untoward change in a patient's condition and to facilitate appropriate intervention by the nursing, medical, or hospital staffs." Because these guidelines are so nebulous, the courts must evaluate each claim of inadequate staffing individually, based on its own merits.

A case that explored the issue of a hospital's failing to have a specially trained nurse on duty was *Northern Trust Company v. Louis A. Weiss Memorial Hospital* (1986). This case involved a baby who was born at 11:35 a.m. Although the amniotic fluid contained a large amount of meconium (indicating that the fetus had been in distress before birth) the baby's Apgar® scores were 7 at one minute and 10 at five minutes. The baby was then taken to the nursery and placed in an isolette. Throughout the evening after her birth, the baby's condition fluctuated: at times, her respiratory rate was as rapid as 150 breaths per minute; at other times, it was normal. The baby also became cyanotic whenever she was removed from the isolette, and her temperature began to climb slightly. The nurse caring for the baby recorded all of her observations. At 3:50 a.m.—about 16 hours after her birth—the baby vomited a large amount of thick, green mucous and continued to have rapid respirations. Her temperature remained slightly elevated. By 5:30 a.m., the baby began having slight retractions, and, 30 minutes later, she vomited brown mucous. At this point, the nurse called the baby's doctor, who then arranged to transfer the baby to another hospital. By the time the baby arrived at the other hospital, she had grunting respirations and was flaccid. She was diagnosed as having Klebsiella sepsis and, despite treatment, she suffered severe brain damage.

The parents sued the hospital, two of the nurses in the nursery, and the doctor. The jury found that the nurses' care had been adequate, but what had been lacking was the supervision of a specially trained nurse who would have been able to judge when an emergency existed and when to notify the doctor. For this, they found the hospital liable.

While this case illustrates the hospital's responsibility for staffing, it also illustrates how variable jury verdicts can be. As discussed in previous chapters, nurses who work in specialty areas are expected to meet the standards of care for those areas. Another jury could have easily found the nurses who cared for the baby negligent for failing to recognize a significant change in the baby's condition and for failing to call the doctor.

As pertains to improper staffing, in most instances, the hospital will be the primary one to be held accountable. After all, it is the hospital's responsibility to hire and train the staff necessary to operate its facility and to close units or beds if staffing needs cannot be met. Even so, staffing continues to be a problem for which hospitals have made a number of excuses. One argument a hospital accused of improper staffing might make is that the nurse-patient ratio at its hospital is the same as at other area hospitals. The court may consider this argument to be valid, as it may choose to let the community set the standard for what constitutes proper staffing, but usually only if patient acuity at the hospitals is comparable. Hospitals may also argue that they are short staffed because no extra nurses are available, or that they do not have adequate funding to boost their staff. However, the courts tend to reject these arguments. Most courts hold the view that, if the hospital cannot hire enough staff, then it should close certain areas and limit admissions.

Of course, chronic understaffing is different than an emergency situation. For example, say that a nurse in a unit has called in sick, and the hospital cannot quickly find a replacement. As a result, other nurses may have to double up on their responsibilities. If a patient is injured in the process, the hospital can reasonably claim that it could not have possibly anticipated the staffing problem, and, therefore, should not be held liable for an error stemming from the shortage.

You need to realize that although the hospital is primarily responsible for staffing shortages, you are not completely free from liability. To begin with, whenever you feel that understaffing exists, you must notify your supervisor or the hospital administration. You must do this each and every time the situation occurs. All too often, nurses become complacent about staff shortages. They start out calling the nursing office to ask for more help, but, time after time, they are told that no help is available. After awhile, they just stop calling. This is a mistake. If a patient is injured on one of those short-staffed shifts, the hospital could later claim that you never told them that you needed help.

Besides calling the nursing office each time you feel understaffing makes patient care unsafe, you need to document that you did so. The New York State Nurses Association has devised a form for documenting just these types of situations. If you do not have such a form, try to have one drawn up for your hospital. In the meantime, simply draft a memorandum after you ave completed your shift. Describe the situation in detail, documenting whom you notified, what that person was told, and the response you received. Send the original to the director of nursing and keep a copy for yourself. The patient's chart or incident reports are not the appropriate places to document a problem with staffing.

Even though you may document each short-staffing situation, you are still not completely relieved of liability. While the courts may take a short-staffed situation into account when considering a claim of malpractice, it will not let you use short staffing as an excuse for your actions. The court will still compare your actions to those that a reasonable nurse would have taken in the same circumstances. If a patient is injured on your shift, you still could be found liable, especially if you

should have been able to foresee the possibility of injury and taken steps to prevent it. If you are acting as charge nurse, you have a responsibility to delegate appropriately and to access all available resources.

The issue of a nurse's negligence in a short-staffing situation was addressed in the case of *Horton v. Niagara Falls Memorial Center* (1976). In this instance, the patient had been admitted to the hospital with pneumonitis. He was placed in a room with a balcony on the hospital's second floor. The staff knew that the man was weak, confused, and uncoordinated. The man's wife stayed with him during much of the afternoon, but, after awhile, she went home. Shortly afterward, construction workers saw the man on the balcony, calling to them and asking for a ladder. The workers notified the unit, and the nurses placed the patient in a Posey® chest restraint and cloth wrist restraints. They then notified the patient's doctor, who told them to make sure that someone stayed with the patient at all times.

The staffing on the unit that night consisted of the charge nurse, one LPN, and one nurse's aide for 19 patients. The nurse called the patient's wife and asked her to come back to the hospital to sit with her husband, saying that no one on the unit was free to do it. The patient's wife, who lived 20 minutes away, said that she would have her mother, who lived only 5 minutes away, come right away. The wife then asked the nurse to have someone else stay with her husband until her mother got there. The nurse replied that they were "understaffed and cannot possibly do that." The charge nurse left the patient unattended, and, by the time the patient's mother-in-law arrived, the patient had again climbed out onto the balcony. This time, though, he fell and injured himself.

At the resulting trial, it was revealed that, of the 19 patients on the unit, ten were in an open ward. Also, just before the patient fell, the charge nurse had allowed the nurse's aid assigned to this particular patient to go to supper. It was also revealed that there was a nurse on orientation that evening who had no patient assignment. Finally, the nurse was not able to show that there was any need on the unit that evening more pressing than the need for someone to stay with this patient. Based on this and other evidence, the court found that the nurse did not exercise reasonable care in safeguarding the patient, and was found liable for the patient's injuries.

The key to the above case is that the nurse did not exercise good judgment in setting priorities and in using the staff available. On the positive side, the case also shows that the courts are at least willing to consider whether a staffing shortage interfered with a nurse's ability to carry out duties. Another case that shows the courts' willingness to consider how staffing affects a nurse's ability to fulfill duty is *HCA Health Services of Midwest, Inc. v. National Bank of Commerce* (1988).

In this case, an apparently healthy infant, named James, was in the hospital nursery. On one particular shift, three nurses were assigned to the nursery to care for James and 18 other babies. The nursery consisted of three connecting rooms divided by walls that were glass from the middle to the top. At the beginning of the shift, two nurses went into one room, where they focused their attention on two premature babies and a baby with jaundice. The third nurse worked with a baby in the admissions room before she went into the third room, where James and six other babies were patients. As soon as the nurse entered the room, she saw James lying face down, not breathing. The staff immediately resuscitated him; however, James suffered brain damage.

At trial, the doctor who assisted in the resuscitation efforts testified that the charge nurse told him that it had been 30 minutes since she had last checked on James. The doctor also testified that he thought that James's mattress, which was old and soft, contributed to James's asphyxia. Finally, he testified that he did not think that James's injury would have occurred if there had been a nurse in the room.

The hospital had a guideline that no baby should be left in a room without a nurse present. The charge nurse testified that she had planned to move all the babies into one room so that the staff could better care for them. However, although she had been on duty an hour and a half before James's arrest, she had not yet done so. The nurse stated that she felt that they were short staffed that shift, and, according to other testimony, hospital administration knew of the need for more nurses in the nursery.

After considering all this evidence, the judge excused the two staff nurses from the lawsuit, found in favor of the charge nurse, and against the hospital. The significance of this verdict is that the court decided that the hospital was negligent because it failed to provide adequate staffing. The court also felt that the charge nurse had reasonably assigned the staff that was available and had not been negligent. Later, the Arkansas Supreme Court sent the case back for a new trial because of certain legal errors. The Supreme Court stated that a jury, not the judge, should decide whether the staff nurses had been negligent. It also stated that, if the jury believed the nurses' versions of what happened, then the nurses should be excused from failing to follow the hospital's policy of having a nurse in every room.

As you can see, based on this case, if you must work in a short-staffed situation, you need to take extra care in setting your priorities. If you make out the work assignment, make sure you use all of your available staff to the best of their abilities. Even if you feel that a short-staffing situation is severe enough to endanger the patient, refusing to accept more patients could result in your being found negligent.

In the case of *In re Mount Sinai Hospital* (1978), three nurses in the intensive care unit refused to accept an admission from the emergency room. The nurses stated that they were already caring for many critically ill patients, and admitting still another one would endanger the ones they already had. The hospital responded by suspending the nurses for three days without pay. The nurses filed suit, but the case was settled in favor of the hospital. The court stated that, if the hospital had to defer to its employees' opinions, it would be placed in an intolerable legal position.

You may be thinking that the courts do not seem to be on your side at all: if you work in a short-staffed situation and a patient becomes injured, you could be held liable; at the same time, if you refuse to accept any new patients because of staffing, you could, again, be blamed. Unfortunately, it is true that the law is heavily weighted in favor of the employer. Sometimes it is better to carry out an assignment as best you can. Remember that the court is most likely going to make the hospital shoulder most of the blame if a patient is injured because of inadequate staffing. You just need to be sure to document each and every time you feel you are working in unsafe conditions, and also to take special care to use the resources you have and set your priorities when providing care.

REFUSING A WORK ASSIGNMENT

The case of *In re Mount Sinai Hospital* (1978)—where the nurses were suspended for refusing to accept new admissions— raises the question as to whether you ever have a right to refuse a work assignment, even if you feel the patient would be endangered. The American Nurses' Association states in its Code for Nurses that nurses must use their professional judgment when they accept responsibilities, seek out advice, or assign responsibilities to others. Taking this one step further, the code tells nurses that if they cannot manage an assignment, then they have a responsibility to either refuse the assignment or to find other ways of making sure that the patient's needs are met. This could be done either by having someone help you or by trading assignments with someone. The code also holds you responsible for asking for help or advice from other health professionals whenever the patient's needs exceed your skills.

But, before you outright refuse to care for a patient, you need to first analyze why you are refusing the assignment. Do you feel the assignment would be unsafe for the patient? Does the assignment require you to assume responsibilities that you are not authorized to perform? Whatever the reason, make sure you have it clear in your mind. Then, talk with your supervisor about the assignment, stating the reasons for your unease. If you do not feel you are competent to complete an assignment, make sure to communicate that. Be willing to work with the supervisor to find a solution to the problem. Again, the solution could be as simple as having another nurse assist you with the procedures with which you are not comfortable.

If your supervisor insists that you take the assignment anyway, document the situation, using the same form that you would use to document a short-staffed situation. Then use your best judgment to decide whether to proceed ahead and complete the assignment to the best of your ability, or to risk suspension or, worse yet, be fired by refusing. This is not an easy situation and, no matter what, you may feel the situation is less than satisfactory.

The key is that you have to make the best decision you can under the circumstances, always keeping the patient's welfare in mind. Oftentimes, you can safely complete an assignment that you think is unfair by using all available resources to assist you in the areas in which you feel uncomfortable. But, you also need to realize that, even taking all of these steps—including documenting the situation does not relieve you of liability if a patient is injured. But, your documentation will show the court the steps you took to alleviate a foreseeable problem.

If the assignment requires you to perform tasks which either the hospital or your state's Board of Nursing specifically prohibits, then you should refuse to perform the assignment. If the hospital disciplines you in some way as a result, you would have grounds to protest the action.

If you are routinely called upon to assume more responsibilities than you feel comfortable with, you may wish to take your protest one step further. This could be through a collective bargaining unit, if one is available for nurses where you work, or through an internal grievance procedure. If the hospital where you work does not have any procedure for dealing with staffing and assignment problems, then it could be found liable in a lawsuit.

The case *Von Stetina v. Florida Medical Center* (1983) involved just such a situation. In this case, a 27-year-old woman was a patient in the intensive care unit and was being maintained on a ventilator. Besides this patient, there were six other patients in the unit, which was staffed with three RNs and an LPN who had floated from another area. During the shift, the unit received five additional admissions. Meanwhile, the first patient became disconnected from her ventilator, arrested, and suffered severe injuries. The patient sued the hospital, claiming that the nurses were too busy with the new admissions to care for her properly, and that the hospital had no policy or procedure regarding short-staffed situations.

At trial, an expert witness testified that the staff on duty could not have safely cared for more than seven patients, the number in the unit before the admissions. The plaintiff also showed that at least three other hospitals in the area could have accepted those five additional patients. The jury found in favor of the plaintiff and awarded her $12,470,000. (The judge, however, decided that this award was excessive and ordered that the case be retried.)

Although you generally do not have a legal right to refuse an assignment as long as you are qualified to perform it, some states do have "conscience laws" that allow you to refuse an assignment based on ethical reasons. Perhaps the best example of this would be a nurse's refusal to participate in an abortion. If you do find yourself involved in such an ethical dilemma, most supervisors would be willing to work with you to adjust the assignment so that you do not have to act against your views. However, before refusing an assignment outright based on this principle, be sure to research whether your state has a law that would protect you. If your state does not, and you refuse the assignment anyway, the hospital would have every right to discipline you.

Once again, the laws pertaining to this area are heavily weighted in favor of the employer. To learn more about this area, check with your state's nursing association to learn its position on accepting or rejecting work assignments. Also, if necessary, ask them for guidance in dealing with your particular situation.

POLICIES ON FLOATING

As one way to solve staffing problems, many hospitals have a policy that requires nurses to occasionally "float" to other areas. Understandably, floating causes many nurses to feel anxious and frustrated—perhaps because they do not like being forced to work in an area they do not enjoy, or because they sincerely feel that their skills are not sharp enough to work competently in that other area. For example, say that you normally work in the intensive care unit, and the hospital wants you to float to pediatrics. You have not worked in pediatrics since nursing school and do not feel comfortable working there now. In this situation, could you safely refuse to float? Probably not.

The only way you should refuse to float is if the assignment would require you to perform procedures that you honestly have never been taught to perform. This does not mean that you just feel rusty; it means that you absolutely have never been taught to perform the required tasks. If it does occur that the hospital wants you to float to an area that would exceed your level of training, take the same steps as you would for refusing any other assignment. First talk with your supervisor and let her know that you have no experience in that area. That way, your supervisor can either change your assignment or arrange for someone else to cover the tasks you do not know how to perform. If your supervisor insists that you fulfill the assignment anyway, then you should refuse. Again, this is only if you would be performing tasks you had never been taught to perform. If you do refuse, you may be dismissed; however, you would probably have grounds to appeal the dismissal in court.

Most hospitals have a policy regarding floating, and you should have been made aware of that policy at the time you were hired. Because hospitals use mandatory floating as a means of meeting staffing demands, you are usually required to comply. One nurse who refused to float spawned the lawsuit of *Francis v. Memorial General Hospital* (1986).

Mr. Francis was a nurse in the intensive care unit of a hospital in New Mexico. On one particular shift, the supervisor instructed him to take charge of the orthopedic unit. Mr. Francis refused,

saying that he did not feel competent. Because of his refusal, the hospital suspended him for two days. When he returned to work, he told the nursing office that he would not float to any area where he felt incompetent. In response, the hospital suspended him indefinitely. In an effort to alleviate the problem, the hospital personnel director offered to orient Mr. Francis to all of the hospital's units so that he would be familiar with the areas if called upon to float. However, Mr. Francis refused. Instead, he requested a hearing to grieve his suspension. This was granted; however, when the hospital told the nurse that he could not bring his lawyer with him to the hearing, Mr. Francis dropped out of the grievance process. The hospital then suspended Mr. Francis permanently. Mr. Francis then filed suit for violation of his civil rights, breach of contract, and wrongful discharge.

At the trial, the court noted that most hospitals have a policy requiring nurses to float, and that Memorial General Hospital had such a policy when Mr. Francis was hired. Mr. Francis argued that he was ethically bound by the state's Nurse Practice Act to refuse to float because he did not feel competent doing so. However, the court countered that Mr. Francis had been given an opportunity to become oriented to other units in the hospital and had refused. It also noted that nurses are bound by their employee manual, and that Mr. Francis had failed to follow the procedures outlined in the manual by not following through with the hospital's grievance procedure. Finally, the court recognized that hospitals require floating so as to provide an adequate staff on all patient units in the most cost-effective manner, which is in the best interest of the public. Both the District Court and the Supreme Court in his state of New Mexico upheld the hospital's right to fire Mr. Francis for his refusal to float.

In conclusion, the courts will most likely look upon floating as a legitimate effort by the hospital to make sure that all of its patients receive adequate care. With this in mind, you can see that you have very little option regarding floating as long as it is a part of your hospital's policy. Again, the best approach would be to perform only those tasks for which you have been trained, and to ask for help and instruction whenever you need it.

MANDATORY OVERTIME

Another way hospitals may try to relieve staffing problems is by asking nurses to work overtime. You have no doubt been in a situation where, at the end of your shift, you learn that the next shift is short staffed. You are extremely tired and want to go home, but the supervisor has asked you to work overtime. You want to refuse, but the supervisor says that there is no one to assume the care of your patients. The supervisor then tells you that, if you leave, you could be charged with abandoning your patients. Is this true?

Not really. But, as always, you still have a responsibility for the patient's welfare. If there is definitely no one available to care for your patients, you cannot just walk away. The only way you legally could do so is if something in your personal life had a higher priority than taking care of your patients. An example of a higher priority would be if you had an obligation to return home to care for a seriously ill family member whos' health would be endangered if you were delayed. Because most nurses do not have these types of personal obligations, they are somewhat bound by their patients' needs.

The point to understand is that hospitals have an obligation to provide each patient with competent nursing care. As an employee—or "servant"—of the hospital, you have a similar obligation. However, the law says that you only need to offer reasonable or minimal assistance if staffing is inadequate. The obvious question here is, "What is reasonable?" Does reasonable mean that the hospital

has a right to expect the nurse to pitch in for another hour or so, or does it mean that the hospital can require the nurse to work another full shift?

Although the answer to this question is not entirely clear, we do know that courts interpret the term "reasonable" to mean "reasonable under the circumstances." This means that, before deciding for patient abandonment, a court would consider all of the facts of the situation. For example, the court might want to know whether the nurse who was asked to work overtime was so physically and mentally exhausted the ability to make decisions would have been compromised. Other questions the court would ask could include: Did the hospital know in advance what the patient load would be for that shift? If so, did it take steps to try and ensure an adequate staff? Did it take other steps to limit its patient population, such as cancel surgery or refer nonemergency admissions to other hospitals?

To further relieve your mind about being charged with abandonment, you should know that this charge is usually leveled against doctors, not nurses. As the chief caretaker of a patient, the doctor has a much stronger legal obligation to the patient's welfare. If a doctor knows that a patient seeking advice is in critical condition, then that doctor has a responsibility to do something, even if it is only to refer the patient to a hospital emergency department. Also, a doctor cannot remove himself or herself from caring for a patient—even if the patient wishes it—if doing so would endanger the patient's well-being. An example of this would be if a patient suffering from a gastrointestinal hemorrhage were to tell the doctor, "Get away from me. You are fired." Obviously, if the doctor walked away, the patient's health would suffer—and the doctor could be charged with abandonment. In such a situation, the doctor would be obliged to stay, to stabilize the patient, and then to seek a replacement.

The first time the concept of abandonment was applied to nurses was in 1968, in the case of *Duling v. Bluefield Sanitarium, Inc.* (1968). In this case, the patient was a 13-year-old girl who had acute rheumatic fever. The girl's mother stated that around 8:00 in the evening, her daughter began to cough violently. The child's condition continued to worsen, and by 9:00, the mother stated that her daughter's heart was beating so loudly that "the mattress shook." Between 8:00 and 9:00, the mother repeatedly asked the nurses to come into the room, but they refused. By 11:00 that night, the child was turning blue. The mother was frantic, but the nurse simply told her, "All she needs is a good night's rest, and if you will sit down and be quiet, she will get it." The mother asked the nurse to call the doctor, but the nurse refused. Sometime later, the nursing supervisor found the mother crying, and immediately went in to help. By that time, it was too late, and the child soon died.

As you can see, abandonment is a gross departure from an acceptable standard of nursing care. For this reason, the charge of abandonment probably would not be brought against a nurse who simply refused to work overtime. At the same time, you still have an obligation to consider the welfare of the patient. If your refusal to remain on duty somehow contributes to the harm of the patient, a court would probably want to know whether you made reasonable arrangements for the continuation of your patient's care. Once again, the exact meaning of what is reasonable is unclear. Furthermore, there is not any case law available that discusses these types of overtime issues.

One case that does address the issue of how the quality of care is affected when a nurse works overtime is *Slatkin v. Capitol Hill Hospital* (1984). In this case, the parents of a 15-month-old child filed a lawsuit against both the nurse and the hospital after their child died. The parents claimed that the nurse caring for their child had turned off the alarms on their child's monitor and that the nurse

then left the child alone for 5 to 10 minutes while she attended to an emergency. The nurse was working two eight-hour shifts, and the child died after the nurse had been on duty for 14 hours. The case was settled out of court, but the parents filed a complaint against the nurse with the state's board of nursing. The board ruled that the nurse had exhibited poor judgment. It filed the finding in the nurse's licensure record, but otherwise took no other action.

Obviously, being fatigued can lead to carelessness, and carelessness can lead to a mistake and a charge of negligence. Unfortunately, there are no hard and fast rules for you to follow when you are in a situation where your supervisor is trying to pressure you into working overtime. Once again, you will have to evaluate each situation—always taking into account what is best for the patient—and make your decision accordingly. To help you further, you may want to check with your hospital union or the nursing associations in your state to see if they have any policies regarding overtime work. For example, the Massachusetts Nurses Association adopted a resolution in 1981 regarding nurses' work assignments. The resolution recognized that chronic, compulsory overtime reduces a nurse's effectiveness and increases the risk of care falling below acceptable standards. The association felt that a nurse has a right to refuse unreasonable demands for overtime.

SOLVING THE PROBLEM

Because chronic understaffing places you in the dilemma of trying to do what is best for the patient while protecting yourself from liability, the best course of action would be to try and alleviate the problem altogether. One option might be to join forces with the other nurses in your hospital to try to bring about change. While some nurses may be nervous about "making waves," they should not be. In this type of situation, there are laws to protect you.

A case that illustrates this fact is *Misericordia Hospital Medical Center v. N.L.R.B.* (1980). In this instance, a charge nurse belonged to a group of hospital employees called the Ad Hoc Patient Care Committee. The JCAHO, in preparation for evaluating the hospital, asked for input from staff members and others as to whether the hospital was meeting accreditation standards. In response, the nurse and committee complained that many shifts were understaffed and that the hospital had failed to remedy the situation. Despite the complaint, the hospital received JCAHO approval, and, soon afterward, it fired the nurse for being "disloyal."

The nurse filed suit, and the National Labor Relations Board (N.L.R.B.) ordered the hospital to reinstate the nurse. The hospital appealed, but the appeals court upheld the order of the N.L.R.B. The court cited a U.S. Supreme Court ruling that employees do not lose protection "when they seek to improve terms and conditions of employment or otherwise improve their lot as employees through channels outside the immediate employee-employer relationship."

Another case where the court ruled similarly was *Frazier v. King* (1989). In this case, a registered nurse was hired to work in the infirmary at Wade Correctional Center. Shortly after she began work, she reported some violations of nursing practice to her supervisor. When her supervisor failed to respond, the nurse went to both the warden and the assistant warden. When the supervisor learned what the nurse had done, she reprimanded the nurse and told her that she could be fired. Nevertheless, about a year later, the nurse spoke with an administrator at the Department of Corrections about the same violations, and also provided documentation. This conversation triggered an investigation, after which the administrator concluded that the nurse's criticisms were well founded.

Despite this, the violations continued, and the nurse again went to the warden to report that, if something was not done she would go to both the Board of Nursing and the media. The warden retorted that he'd fire her if she did. The nurse went to the Board of Nursing anyway, and the Board charged the supervisor with violating the state's Nursing Practice Act. Shortly afterward, the nurse was fired. She appealed her termination, and the court ordered her reinstated, saying that the termination violated her rights to speak out about the nursing practices where she worked. Not stopping there, the nurse then filed a civil rights action against all those responsible for her termination, alleging the termination violated her rights under the First and Fourteenth Amendments. Again, the court ruled in her favor.

As you can see, you do have some freedom for trying to effect a change in your working environment. Just be sure to use whatever channels are available in your hospital for voicing your complaints. Be clear about your complaint, and provide proper documentation of exact situations in which you feel you were forced to work in an understaffed or unsafe situation. Do not be discouraged if you do not receive an immediate response. Continue on and pursue your complaint to the upper levels of hospital management. If you still do not receive a satisfactory response, and you feel the unsafe conditions constitute an unsafe labor practice, you should contact the N.L.R.B.

CHAPTER 5

Questions 54–62

54. If you are making an assignment on an understaffed shift, the law allows you to

   a. refuse to begin the shift until more help is sent.

   b. forbid anyone from the previous shift to leave.

   c. make the assignment as best you can, knowing you cannot be held liable.

   d. omit tasks that are not absolutely necessary.

55. When making a work assignment, a nurse is legally responsible for

   a. only making sure that all patients have been assigned.

   b. making the assignment in such a way that no staff nurse is overworked.

   c. making the assignment in such a way that all of the patients' needs will be met.

   d. making sure that all care delivered is above average.

56. As a charge nurse, if you realize a nurse in your area is delivering inadequate care, the law holds you

   a. not responsible.

   b. responsible for intervening to protect the patient, but only if you witness a negligent act.

   c. responsible for intervening to protect the patient, whether you see the negligent act or not.

   d. responsible for seeing that the nurse is fired.

57. With regard to adequate staffing, the JCAHO has

   a. set specific guidelines for what is considered adequate.

   b. demanded that all hospitals maintain certain nurse-patient ratios.

   c. stated only that enough nurses must be on duty to give patients good care.

   d. has said nothing about the issue.

58. If the situation of chronic understaffing is an issue in a case, who is most likely to be found liable?

   a. the nurse

   b. the doctor

   c. the hospital

   d. no one, because the court will dismiss the claim

59. Notifying your supervisor each time you find yourself in a short-staffed situation

   a. relieves you of all liability if a patient is subsequently injured.

   b. relieves you of liability, unless the negligent act that injures the patient had nothing to do with staffing.

   c. forces the hospital to share half the blame.

   d. relieves you of nothing; the court will consider the staffing situation but will still hold you accountable for delivering an appropriate standard of care.

60. The only situation in which you could safely refuse an assignment and have the courts support you would be if

    a. you feel your skills in that area are stale.

    b. you feel that the assignment gives you too many patients to care for.

    c. the patient in question has a communicable disease.

    d. the assignment requires you to perform tasks that either the hospital or your state's Board of Nursing prohibit.

61. What is the court's general position on "floating"?

    a. that floating is illegal

    b. that floating is illegal unless the hospital had the policy before 1980

    c. that floating may be necessary, but that a nurse may refuse to float if she feels her skills are "rusty"

    d. that floating is a legal and acceptable way to relieve staffing shortages

62. If you work to improve conditions at your place of employment, what kind of protection does the law provide?

    a. None; the hospital can fire you if it wishes.

    b. Limited protection, but only if you have been employed for more than ten years.

    c. You are protected from being fired, but only if you work through your immediate supervisor to improve conditions.

    d. You are protected even if you work through channels outside your immediate supervisor to improve conditions.

CHAPTER 6

UNDERSTANDING A PATIENT'S RIGHTS

CHAPTER OBJECTIVE

After studying this chapter, the reader will be aware of the basic rights that patients have and recognize situations that jeopardize those rights.

LEARNING OBJECTIVES

After reading this chapter, the reader will be able to

1. describe a situation in which a health care provider could be found guilty of fraudulent concealment.

2. define the meaning of informed consent.

3. identify the person responsible for obtaining a patient's informed consent.

4. describe two situations in which a patient's consent would no longer be valid.

5. identify three criteria a patient must satisfy to be able to exercise the right to refuse treatment.

6. describe two situations in which an informed consent would not be necessary.

7. describe the legal consequences of continuing to administer treatment after a patient has refused the treatment.

8. identify four instances in which a court would override a patient's right to refuse treatment.

9. describe the only situation in which a health care provider can legally fail to resuscitate a patient.

10. identify who is qualified to give consent for a comatose patient.

11. identify the situation in which a living will becomes effective.

12. name three situations that could trigger a patient's lawsuit for invasion of privacy.

13. identify four situations when the courts permit the release of confidential information.

Overshadowing all of your nursing activities is your duty to the patient. It has already been established that the patient has a right to receive care consistent with professional standards. You also need to realize that the patient has other rights, too. These include the right to determine the course of treatment, the right to information about all aspects of treatment, the right to privacy, and the right to refuse treatment.

The courts and the law recognize the patient's basic rights, and you're expected to honor them. You are also expected to uphold patients' rights listed by your hospital or published by professional organizations, such as the National League of Nursing. Many state legislatures, as well as the federal government, are seeking to adopt patient bills of rights in response to the public's outcry. It is important for the nurse to recognize that a patients perception of the health care system is influenced by the negative impact of managed care and their perception that the health care industry is putting profit over patients.

PATIENT'S RIGHT TO INFORMATION

The law has been clear that a patient has a right to information regarding health and treatment. Legislation released late in 2000 under the Health Insurance Portability and Accountability Act (HIPAA) further defines a patient's rights in the area of privacy, confidentiality and access to their medical records. The law does not clearly articulate the nurse's responsibility for this aspect of patient care.

In the past, it has been common practice for the doctor to be responsible for explaining all aspects of care to the patient and to his or her family. However, this is changing. As more patients begin to take charge of their own care, they are seeking information from health care providers other than their doctors. And, because nurses are often much more accessible than doctors, patients are turning to them for advice. But, in at least one instance described in the case of *Tuma v. Board of Nursing* (1979)—a nurse provided a patient with information that the patient requested and ended up in a legal battle.

Jolene Tuma, a nursing instructor at the College of Southern Idaho, supervised nursing students at the hospital. On one occasion, she was assigned to a patient with myelogenous leukemia who had been admitted to the hospital for chemotherapy. The patient was quite distressed about receiving chemotherapy, and she asked Ms. Tuma about possible alternatives. Ms. Tuma discussed alternative treatments in detail with the patient, including laetrile therapy and natural food and herbal remedies. She compared the side effects of each of the therapies to those of chemotherapy,

and offered to arrange an appointment with a therapist who practiced alternative therapies. Throughout the discussions, Ms. Tuma never encouraged the patient to seek alternative therapy or to discontinue chemotherapy. The patient then asked Ms. Tuma to tell her son and daughter-in-law about the alternative treatments, which she did. In turn, they told the patient's doctor. Because of the patient's questions, the doctor again discussed the purposes of chemotherapy with her, after which the patient agreed to continue on the prescribed medical regimen. Two weeks later, she died.

The doctor then demanded that Ms. Tuma be fired. At the hospital's request, the Board of Nursing investigated the situation. The Board stated that Ms. Tuma's behavior had been unprofessional because she had interfered with the doctor-patient relationship. As a result, they suspended her nursing license for six months.

Ms. Tuma appealed and lost. She appealed again. This time, the State Supreme Court ruled that she could not be found guilty of unprofessional conduct because the state's Nurse Practice Act did not clearly define unprofessional conduct and did not provide guidelines for avoiding such conduct.

Even though Ms. Tuma finally won her case, it does not help solve the nurse's problem of knowing how to uphold the patient's right to information without encountering legal difficulties. In the above case, the patient had asked Ms. Tuma, not her doctor, about the alternative therapies. In addition, the doctor admitted in court that he did not know anything about these therapies. So, it stands to reason that if the doctor would not have been able to provide the patient with the information that she had requested, then the nurse should have been allowed to. Another factor to consider is that perhaps, in the three years it took before the case was finally resolved, the court's understanding of the responsibility of the nurse to the patient had become more clear.

The patient's right to information does not stop with an explanation of his or her illness. The patient has a right to know everything about received care, including when a mistake has been made. In fact, if a health care provider withholds information to try and cover up a mistake, then that health care provider may be guilty of fraudulent concealment. Again, this normally applies to doctors, but nurses may also be held accountable. An example of a case where this happened is *Garcia v. Presbyterian Hospital Center* (1979).

In this case, the patient underwent two different surgeries for prostate cancer in the same year. The next year, the doctor readmitted him for still another surgery. The patient repeatedly asked both the doctor and the hospital nursing staff why the third surgery was necessary, but no one would ever answer his questions. Some time later, the patient learned that a catheter had been inadvertently left behind during the second surgery, thus necessitating the third operation. By the time the patient learned about the mistake, the statute of limitations for filing a lawsuit had expired. The patient filed suit anyway, and the court ruled that, because information had been withheld from the patient, the statute of limitations would not bar him from filing suit. The court further stated that the hospital had an obligation to divulge all material facts to its patients.

In another case, *Bourassa v. LaFortuna* (1989), the court stated that a nurse does not have the same duty to disclose information to a patient as does a doctor. This case involved a patient who died during a surgical procedure. Three years after the patient's death, the patient's wife filed suit, claiming that the surgeon, the anesthesiologist, and the nurse anesthetist conspired to conceal the facts surrounding her husband's death. It was while deciding whether the statute of limitations for filing suit should be extended that the court rendered its opinion about a nurse's responsibility to divulge information to a patient. In fact, besides stating that nurses do not have the same responsibility as do physicians to disclose information, it also stated that nurses should not be encouraged to give information to a patient without the direction of a treating physician.

Once again, it seems the courts have not sent a clear and consistent message to nurses regarding their responsibilities in this area. As a nurse, what are your responsibilities and your limitations as far as providing information to the patient? While there are no black and white rules, there are guidelines, such as those published by your hospital and the National League of Nursing regarding patient rights. Study those guidelines, and, while you are caring for a patient, continually assess his or her need for more information regarding illness or treatment. If you feel that the patient needs more information, use your best professional judgment to decide whether you, or the doctor, should be the one to provide it.

INFORMED CONSENT

Along with the patient's right to information about his or her illness and its treatment, the patient has a right to decide what type of treatment to undergo, if any. This right forms the basis of informed consent. But the process of informed consent involves more than just asking the patient whether she or he wants to undergo a certain procedure or receive a certain treatment. In fact, the process of informed consent involves several important steps, and it is important to understand each of these steps—and to know who is responsible for implementing them—to make sure that the patient's rights are honored.

To begin with, the law says that a patient must give consent for any care received. Actually, even touching a patient against his or her will may constitute battery. But the court makes certain allowances for basic care. For example, the court assumes that by allowing admission into a hospital, the patient has given consent for basic, routine care, such as vital signs. The court also assumes that when you explain other procedures or treatments to the patient, any competent, conscious patient could refuse the procedure at that time. If not refused, then you are free to proceed. For example, when you are preparing to insert a Foley catheter in a patient, you would first tell the patient the purpose of the procedure and what the procedure entails. Then, if the patient did not refuse to have the procedure, you would be free to proceed.

More invasive procedures require an informed consent. Basically, an informed consent means that the patient has received—in readily understandable terms—all of the information any reasonable person would need to make a decision regarding a treatment or procedure. Procedures that require an informed consent include any medical or surgical procedures that are invasive, experimental, unlikely to succeed, or pose a risk of injury. Specific examples include major or minor surgery, procedures requiring anesthesia, radiation therapy, blood transfusions, and nonsurgical procedures that involve more than a slight risk of harm, such as certain medications, chemotherapy, hormone therapy, myelograms, intravenous pyelograms, and arteriograms. Experimental proceedings or care or treatment provided under a research protocol require a heightened level of consent.

The person responsible for explaining a procedure to a patient and obtaining the patient's consent is the doctor—usually the doctor who will perform the procedure—not the nurse. In case after case, the courts have ruled that this is the doctor's duty and that it cannot be delegated to a nurse. However, if you choose to assume the responsibility of obtaining a patient's informed consent, then you need to know that you are taking on more responsibility than is required. Keep in mind that many lawsuits are based on the allegation that the patient either did not consent to a procedure or did not

understand the explanation of what the procedure entailed or the risks involved.

For a patient to be truly informed, they must receive a description of the proposed procedure or treatment, know the name and qualifications of the person who will perform the procedure, understand the expected outcome and likelihood of success, and be aware of the risks. In addition, an explanation of the alternatives to this particular treatment or procedure as well as the possible effect of no treatment at all must be given. The patient also needs to be informed that if they refuse to have this treatment or procedure, other care or support will not be withdrawn. Finally, once consent is given, the patient can withdraw consent at any time before the procedure or treatment is performed.

As you can see, this is a serious responsibility, and not one to be taken lightly. When talking with the patient, the doctor has to decide exactly how much information to reveal based on that patient's level of education, understanding, and emotional state. Occasionally, the doctor may feel that certain information may actually jeopardize a patient's health. If so, the doctor can legally withhold this information under the doctrine of therapeutic privilege.

For the most part though, the patient is entitled to as much information as can be comprehended. And, perhaps of foremost concern to most patients are the risks of a procedure. Of course, it is not necessary, and not even practical, to discuss each and every possible complication that could result from a procedure. The risks that are important to discuss are those known as material risks.

Exactly which risks are material risks varies with the patient and the procedure. At trial, the court usually requires an expert witness to help identify which risks are material risks. If a risk occurs frequently or is particularly severe, then this may identify it as being a material risk. However, a material risk may also be one that would markedly alter a patient's physical appearance or sexual or reproductive functioning. The best guideline, though, for determining which risks are material risks would be to ask yourself if a reasonable person in similar circumstances would refuse to have the procedure or operation knowing the risk.

A case in which the patient claimed to have been uninformed about a material risk is *Scaria v. St. Paul Fire and Marine Insurance Company* (1975). The patient in this case had been admitted to the hospital for an aortogram because of a history of hypertension. According to the patient, he asked the doctor about the risks of the procedure, and the doctor replied that there was a possibility of a clot forming at the injection site. When the patient questioned what would occur if that happened, the doctor told him that the clot could be easily removed. The patient stated that he then asked, "Is that all?" and that the doctor responded, "That's all."

The patient underwent the aortogram and suffered complications that rendered him paralyzed. At the trial, the doctor defended himself by saying that he had informed the patient of more risks than the patient had related. But the patient stated that, if he had been told about all of the possible complications, he would not have had the procedure, or he would have at least talked with his brother first, who was a doctor. The court found the doctor liable for failure to obtain an informed consent because he did not provide the patient with information that a reasonable patient would want to know. However, the court also stated that a doctor was not required to discuss risks that are apparent or known to the patient, or of such remote possibility that the discussion would only falsely alarm the patient.

While you may not be responsible for obtaining an informed consent, many hospitals require nurses to witness the signing of the consent. By signing your name as a witness, you are simply saying that you saw the patient sign the consent form and that the patient appeared awake, alert, and aware of what he or she was signing. You are also witnessing that the patient was not coerced into consenting to the procedure, either by the doctor or by the patient's family. Acting as a witness does not mean that you have a duty to provide the patient with the information needed to make an informed consent. Again, this is the doctor's responsibility. In fact, you do not even have to be present when the doctor explains the procedure to the patient.

A case where a patient tried to blame the nurse for failing to provide necessary information is *Robertson v. Menorah Medical Center* (1979). In this case, the patient was admitted to the hospital for a vaginal hysterectomy. After the surgery, the patient developed a fistula between her bladder and vagina, which required two operations to repair. Besides filing a lawsuit against the surgeon, she also sued the hospital claiming that the hospital and its nurses had a duty to explain the risks and possible complications of the hysterectomy to her and also to tell her about alternative methods of treatment. Although the patient signed a printed hospital consent form, she stated that she had not read all of it and that no one had explained it to her. After hearing all the evidence, the court stated that the hospital had no duty to inform the patient of the risks of the procedure. The court also found that the nurse who had witnessed the signing of the consent form had no reason to suspect that the patient was not informed about the procedure. The court emphasized that the duty to provide a patient with information rests with the health care provider who orders, or will perform, the treatment.

Despite this, you should still clarify what the doctor told the patient and answer any questions that you feel comfortable answering. However, you should always refer any questions dealing with informed consent back to the doctor. If the patient seems confused about explanations received, and you do not clarify things, then you have a duty to document your observations in the patient's chart and make sure that the patient receives the information from someone else, such as the doctor or another appropriate source.

Consider a situation in which it is the last few minutes before surgery. You are just about to give the patient his preoperative medication and he or she says something that causes you to question whether the patient understands the scheduled procedure. Is this significant? You bet it is. It means that the patient's consent is no longer valid. You should hold the preoperative medication and immediately notify the patient's doctor. The doctor then has an obligation to come and discuss the procedure with the patient again and secure an informed consent.

A consent may also become invalid if the patient's medical condition changes in such a way as to alter the risks and benefits of the procedure. For example, if a patient scheduled for elective coronary bypass surgery suddenly develops severe hypertension, then the risks of the surgery could be increased. In such a situation, the doctor must explain the new risks and benefits of the surgery to make sure that the patient still gives consent. The same thing goes for a patient who has refused a certain procedure: If a patient's condition changes and alters the risks and benefits of a procedure, then that patient has a right to be reappraised of the situation and again decide for or against the procedure.

You are also responsible for making sure that the patient has made an informed consent before a procedure is performed. For example, it is common practice for nurses to check patients' charts to make sure that the patient has signed a consent before going to surgery. Remember that performing a procedure without the patient's informed consent constitutes battery. Although the courts usually will not hold the hospital responsible if the patient sues for battery for performing surgery without a consent, it

could hold you responsible if you assisted with the procedure or if you knew it was taking place and did not stop it. The same thing goes for failure to provide adequate information for consent. If you know that the doctor has not provided the patient with the information needed to make an informed consent, then you must try and stop the procedure by informing your supervisor.

A case that puts an interesting twist on this aspect of the law is *Fiorentino v. Wagner* (1967). The patient in this instance was a 14-year-old boy who had been admitted to the hospital for surgical treatment of scoliosis. As it turns out, the surgeon who was to perform the surgery did not use the medically accepted procedure for the surgery. For the previous 5 years, whenever he performed this type of surgery, he used a procedure unique only to him. But, the results of those surgeries were less than optimal. Of the 35 surgeries he had performed, 5 patients had suffered serious complications. In fact, just the year before, the surgeon had been barred from using a certain hospital after one of his patients became paralyzed as a result of his procedure. The parents were not aware of this history; neither the doctor nor the hospital told them. The surgeon performed the procedure on their son, and the boy died as a result. The parents sued, and the court found both the doctor and the hospital liable. The court stated that, first of all, the doctor had an obligation to let the parents know that his procedure was unorthodox and that there were risks to its use. Furthermore, the court felt, because the hospital knew that the proposed surgery was not recognized as an accepted method for correcting scoliosis, and also knew of the doctor's surgical record, that it, too, had an obligation to make sure that the surgeon disclosed this information.

Another thing to consider is who is qualified to give consent. Any competent, alert adult should always be the one to give consent for treatment. But what if the patient is receiving medications that impair mental function, such as sedatives or narcotics? Then make sure the doctor is aware of the patient's medication schedule and the discussion with the patient is timed so that it occurs when the patient will be alert. Otherwise, the doctor will be responsible for evaluating the patient's mental status to determine whether the patient is alert enough to understand the explanation of the procedure and to give consent. Documentation of that evaluation, in this instance, will be an important component of the informed consent process for this patient.

If the patient is comatose for a long period of time, the doctor may ask the court to appoint a guardian, who would then be authorized to give consent for certain procedures. But if the patient's condition has occurred more recently, and the patient requires immediate treatment, the doctor may ask the nearest relative, usually the spouse, for consent. It is important to note here that exactly who the court considers to be the next of kin varies from state to state. Even though consulting the next of kin may be practical, it does not protect the doctor if the patient later gains consciousness and decides to sue.

The doctor may also consult the patient's nearest relative if the patient is incompetent to make a decision regarding their own care. Incompetence, of course, is difficult to determine, both by doctors and by courts. If a court declares a patient incompetent, then it will appoint a guardian who will be the only one authorized to give consent for the patient's treatment. On occasion, a doctor may ask a court to appoint a guardian for a patient, particularly if the doctor is not comfortable with the decisions being made by the patient's next of kin.

It is important not to confuse mental illness with incompetence. A diagnosis of mental illness, and even involuntary institutionalization for mental illness, does not automatically mean that a patient is incompetent to make decisions regarding health care. This right is so extensive that a patient may even refuse medication that has been prescribed to

treat the mental illness. The only situations in which a patient can be forced to take the drugs are in an emergency when the patient runs a risk of self-harm or harm to others, or when the medication is necessary to keep the patient's condition from significantly and suddenly deteriorating.

When minors are concerned, the doctor must usually obtain consent from the parents. Most states define a minor as one who is less than 18 years old. However, some states allow minors to consent to their own treatment if they are emancipated. An emancipated minor is one who is married, a parent, pregnant, or financially independent. Many states also allow minors to give consent for certain types of treatment, such as for alcohol and drug abuse or a sexually transmitted disease. If the doctor considers the minor to be mature, the minor may have the right to consent to or refuse emergency care, obtain contraceptives and advice about contraception, or obtain an abortion (although the parents may have to be notified about the last two).

A final aspect of informed consent to consider is when an informed consent is not necessary. The first situation whereby a doctor may proceed without informed consent is if the patient has waived this right. After all, a patient's rights include the right not to be informed. If the patient has told the doctor that he or she does not want to know the details of treatment, and the doctor has made it clear to the patient that risks and alternatives do exist, then an informed consent would not be necessary. Such a statement made by a patient should always be documented in the medical record.

The second exception to the requirement for an informed consent is when an emergency exists. The courts define an emergency as a situation in which the patient is at risk for losing life, a limb, an organ, or function. In these types of situations, when the patient is not conscious and cannot give consent, or when the patient is a minor and the doctor cannot reach the parents, then the doctor can proceed without an informed consent. In emergencies, the law assumes that, if the patient were able, consent to treatment would be given.

This exception does not apply if the doctor has reason to believe that the patient would not authorize the treatment if able. For example, say that the patient has refused this type of treatment in the past. The exception also does not apply if the doctor can wait for proper consent without increasing the patient's risk. For this reason, if the doctor proceeds with treatment without an informed consent, it should be thoroughly documented, specifying the risks the patient would face without treatment.

If you are asked to assist with such treatment, but you feel the doctor could safely wait for an informed consent, then tell the doctor, along with the reasons for feeling as you do. If the doctor insists on proceeding, and wants you to assist, what should you do? Again, you are going to have to use your professional judgment to evaluate the situation. If you think the patient may be harmed if you refuse to help, you should go ahead and assist. But if you do not think the patient would be endangered, you should refuse to assist and notify your supervisor.

RIGHT TO REFUSE TREATMENT

Just as a patient has a right to consent to treatment, there exists a right to refuse it. You need to honor this right, even if the patient's refusal could lead to death. The common law right of an individual to protect his or her body from unwanted invasion and the constitutional right of privacy form the foundation of this right. Also, the Patient Self Determination Act clearly defines the circumstances by which a patient can elect the type of treatment received or refused.

But, before honoring a wish to withhold or withdraw treatment, doctors and other health care providers must first determine that several criteria exist. The first of these is that the patient is mentally competent. For the patient to be incompetent, he or she must lack the mental ability necessary to make an informed decision. For example, a delirious or hallucinating patient probably would not be considered competent. Even so, a court would require proof, including documentation in the medical record of the patient's actions, before declaring a patient incompetent. However, the refusal itself— even if it does not make sense to you or to any other member of the health care team—cannot be a reason for declaring a patient incompetent. For example, in *Lane v. Candura* (1994), a 77-year-old woman who had gangrene in her foot and lower leg refused to have her leg amputated, as recommended by her doctor. The patient's daughter asked the court to appoint her temporary guardian of her mother so that she could give the necessary consent for surgery. The court refused, stating that a competent person can reject treatment even if a reasonable person would have consented. Therefore, even though the patient refused what could have been a life-preserving procedure, the court stated that the patient was competent and had a right to make that decision.

Besides making sure that the patient is competent, the doctor needs to be certain that the patient is fully aware of his or her condition and prognosis and of the risks involved in stopping or refusing treatment. The doctor's discussion with the patient should also include a description of alternative treatments that are available. If the patient continues to refuse treatment, the doctor then needs to make sure that the patient is making the decision voluntarily and is not being forced into it by someone else, such as a relative.

If all of these criteria are met, you can feel sure that the patient has a right to refuse treatment, even emergency or life-saving treatment. If the doctor or the hospital disregards those rights and administers treatment anyway, the patient would have grounds for a lawsuit. A case where a doctor ignored a patient's refusal for treatment and was later found liable is *Estate of Leach v. Shapiro* (1984). In this case, the patient had specifically told the hospital and her doctor that she did not want to be kept alive by machines. However, when she suffered a complete cardiac arrest, her doctor vigorously resuscitated her and placed her on a ventilator without first consulting her family. The family sued for invasion of privacy, pain and suffering, mental anguish, additional medical expenses, and punitive damages. The court ruled against the doctor, stating that the treatment of a patient without consent, even if the treatment is beneficial, constitutes a battery.

The court made a similar decision in the case of *Bartling v. Superior Court (Glendale Adventist Medical Center)* (1984). This time the patient was a 70-year-old man with chronic lung disease and a malignant lung tumor. He had been placed on a ventilator and, when he repeatedly tried to disconnect the tubing, was placed in restraints. Despite the patient's serious medical condition, the doctor had not diagnosed the patient as being terminally ill. Therefore, a living will would have had no effect, because living wills only concern situations wherein the patient is terminal. (Living wills will be discussed in greater detail later in this chapter.) When the hospital refused to honor both the patient's and his wife's requests to discontinue the life support, the wife sought a court order. The court stated that the patient had a constitutional right to refuse medical treatment, and when a doctor persisted in administering treatment against the patient's wishes, it was considered battery.

While both of these cases involve doctors, you need to realize that nurses, too, can be accused of battery if they administer treatment that the patient refuses. Even if the doctor ordered the treatment, you still could be held liable. Consider, for example, a situation in which the doctor ordered a straight catheterization for a urine sample. When you go in to perform the procedure, the patient

refuses and tells you to go away. If you persist, and perform the catheterization anyway, then you could be found guilty of battery. Battery does not mean that you held the patient down and forcibly administered a procedure; it just means that you performed the procedure against the patient's wishes.

Perhaps the best publicized case concerning a patient's right to refuse or discontinue treatment was the case involving Karen Ann Quinlan. Karen Quinlan was comatose with an irreversible brain injury from which she had no hope of recovery; however, she was not legally brain dead. Although Karen's parents wanted her life-support treatment discontinued, her doctors refused unless the courts would support their action. Her parents took the matter all the way to the Supreme Court of New Jersey, which ruled that the life-support treatment could be discontinued as long as the hospital's ethics committee, the patient's attending physician, the patient's guardian, and the patient's family agreed.

Since the Quinlan case, which occurred in 1976, the courts in numerous other states have dealt with similar issues. And time after time, the courts have supported the patient's right to choose. Of course, it is always best if the patient has previously expressed a choice regarding medical treatment. If the patient had never expressly conveyed such wishes to his or her family, and can no longer speak these wishes, then the court must consider whether the person speaking for the patient is representing what the patient would wish to have happen and whether the decision is consistent with reasonable medical judgment. With this in mind, courts have upheld a patient's right to refuse artificial ventilation, dialysis, intravenous medications, amputations, and even artificial nutrition.

In another case, *Cruzan v. Director, Missouri Department of Health* (1990), the Supreme Court of the United States held that individual states could require life sustaining treatment to be continued unless there was "clear and convincing evidence" that the patient (had they been competent) would have refused such treatment. This ruling should encourage patients to consider the type of care they would wish should they become incapacitated and should execute specific advance directives mentioning particular treatments and situations. These discussions should occur between the individual and his or her physician as well as family so that there will be no room for dispute as to the appropriate care to provide should a person, by virtue of illness be unable to articulate such wishes.

An example of a case where a federal court stated that there is no difference between artificial feeding and other life-support measures is *Gray v. Romeo* (1988). In this case, Mrs. Gray had been a healthy, energetic woman until she suddenly suffered a massive cerebral hemorrhage. Mrs. Gray's husband consented to emergency surgery, which established that Mrs. Gray had suffered severe damage to her right cerebral hemisphere. Despite all treatment, Mrs. Gray never regained consciousness. About two weeks later, Mr. Gray consented to the insertion of a gastrostomy tube so that Mrs. Gray could be fed directly into her stomach. The artificial feedings continued for the next year and a half. At that time, Mrs. Gray's family asked that the doctor stop the feedings so that Mrs. Gray would be allowed to die. Both the hospital and the Director of the Department of Mental Health and Retardation and Hospitals for that state refused. Mr. Gray subsequently filed a lawsuit alleging that the hospital was violating Mrs. Gray's civil rights. The court agreed. The court stated that the gastrostomy tube was a form of medical treatment, which the patient had the right to refuse. Furthermore, it found that, while the maintenance of the gastrostomy tube may not be extraordinary or invasive, maintaining a person on artificial feeding over an extended period is both intrusive and extraordinary. In making its decision, the court reasoned that

deliberately ending a life by removing artificial means is different from allowing nature to take its course.

Another area that has formed the basis of many legal actions is the patient's refusal of blood transfusions because of certain religious beliefs. For example, Jehovah's Witnesses oppose blood transfusions based on a passage in the Bible that forbids "drinking" of blood. Some members of this religion believe that receiving a transfusion will deprive them of everlasting life. The courts have repeatedly upheld a patient's right to refuse a transfusion based on these principles. Just one example is *In re Melido* (1976). In this instance, a 23-year-old woman who was a Jehovah's Witness refused a blood transfusion that the doctor felt was necessary to save her life. The hospital sought the court's permission to administer the transfusion anyway, but the court refused. The court stated that an adult of sound mind cannot be forced to receive medical treatment against her will "unless the state can show a compelling overriding interest."

So, what constitutes a "compelling overriding interest" by the state? One example would be if the patient's decision would cause injury to an innocent third party. For example, in the above case, the court stated that it may have ruled differently if the patient had been a parent of a minor child. Then, if the patient had died as a result of her refusal of treatment, the child would be injured because of the loss of a caretaker.

Another example of an innocent third party being injured would be if a patient were pregnant and her refusal of treatment would endanger the life of her unborn child. For example, in *Jefferson v. Griffin Spalding County Hospital Authority* (1981), a pregnant patient with a complete placenta previa refused to consent to a Cesarean section. In response, the court awarded custody of the fetus to the guardian who was authorized to make decisions to safeguard the fetus. This award included authority to consent to a surgical delivery.

Another instance that involves a third party is when parents make decisions regarding their child's treatment. When the life or health of a child is at stake, the courts tend to rule differently. Even if the parents are Jehovah's Witnesses and they have refused to give permission for the hospital to administer a blood transfusion to their child, the court is likely to override the parent's decision, especially if the situation is life threatening. If the situation is not life threatening, the court will probably uphold the parents' right to refuse.

One such instance where this occurred is documented in the case of *In re Green* (1972). Here, the mother of a 16-year-old boy consented to surgery to correct her son's scoliosis; however, she made her consent contingent upon the hospital's assurance that the boy would not be given a blood transfusion. The hospital refused to agree to such a stipulation and took the matter to court, requesting that the minor be declared a neglected child and that a guardian be appointed. The court refused, stating that the child's condition was not life threatening and that the state's interest was not great enough to override the parent's religious beliefs.

When religious beliefs are not involved, a court is more likely to rule against the parents, especially if the situation is serious. One such case, *In re Minor* (1978), involved the parents of a 2-year-old child diagnosed as having acute leukemia. The parents wanted to discontinue the boy's chemotherapy regimen and instead treat him with Laetrile®. When the case was brought before the court, the court ruled that the child was a neglected child. The court ordered that the child be made a ward of the court and placed back on chemotherapy.

And yet another situation in which the state's interests are involved and would override the patient's right to refuse treatment would be if the patient has a communicable disease. Obviously, if the patient refused treatment, then many other people could be infected. Another example of this is the law that requires school-age children to receive polio vaccine before they can enter public school.

Besides these situations—when the patient is incompetent, when a third party is involved, or when the public welfare could be harmed—the court may also override a patient's refusal of treatment if the court is convinced that the patient has otherwise expressed strong feelings that would seem to contradict refusal. For example, consider a situation in which a patient, who has refused to have a blood transfusion because of religious beliefs, has hinted to you that she or he would not prevent the transfusion as long as the court took responsibility and ordered it. This is the type of situation that occurred in *in re President of Georgetown College*. In this case, the court ordered that a 25-year-old female patient, who was a mother of a minor child, be administered a life-saving transfusion after the patient indicated to the judge that if the court made the decision about the transfusion, she would not be morally responsible for having received the blood.

Now that you know that the patient has a right to refuse treatment, what should you do if you are caring for a patient who suddenly refuses any further treatment? The first thing you should do is stop what you are doing, especially if you are preparing to administer some type of treatment that the patient refuses. Then you should immediately notify your supervisor. It is important not to delay at this point, because, if you do, and the patient's condition worsens because of your delay, you could be found liable. The supervisor will then be responsible for notifying the doctor. The doctor should come and talk with the patient. If the patient continues to refuse care, then the doctor should have the patient sign a form relieving the hospital and health care team of liability. If the patient refuses to sign, the doctor may try to get the patient's next of kin to sign. Either way, be sure to thoroughly document the situation in the patient's record, including if the patient has refused to sign a release.

Another situation in which you may find yourself is when the doctor has ordered that a patient's life support equipment be discontinued. If you are asked to help terminate the equipment, make sure that you completely understand your state's right-to-die laws. The reason for this is that some states feel there is a difference between the refusal of treatment and the withdrawal of treatment. Even if the patient requests a cessation of treatment and has signed a release, you could be prosecuted on criminal charges if your state laws do not allow you to take this action. On the other hand, if the patient's family has requested that the support be terminated, and you refuse, you could be charged with battery. Therefore, to protect yourself, make sure you know what the law in your state has to say about this matter.

PATIENT'S DISCHARGE AGAINST MEDICAL ADVICE

Along with the patient's right to refuse treatment, he or she has a right to check out of the hospital against medical advice (AMA) at any time and for any reason, provided that the patient is competent to make such a decision. If you attempt to detain a patient after a decision to leave, you could be charged with false imprisonment or unlawful restraint.

Perhaps the best way of dealing with this type of situation is to try to prevent it from occurring. If the patient has become withdrawn or hostile, and may be planning to leave the hospital, try to talk with the patient. Sometimes, just by listening, you can discover a problem that you, or someone else, can solve.

If the patient insists on leaving, check your hospital's policy for handling this situation and follow it to the letter. The basic steps include contacting your supervisor, the patient's family, or other responsible person; explaining the AMA procedures; and giving the patient the AMA form to sign. You need to make sure that the patient is competent to make a decision and is aware of the medical risks of this action. Inform the patient that alternative treatments at the hospital exist; these may include treatment at other hospitals or area clinics. If the patient refuses to sign the form, document that, as well as your conversation with the patient and his family, in the medical record.

The patient's leaving AMA does not relieve you of your responsibility for discharge planning and patient teaching. Follow your usual routine for discharging a patient, including accompanying the patient to the front door of the hospital and arranging for necessary follow-up care.

An example of a case involving a charge of false imprisonment is *Big Town Nursing Home v. Newman* (1970). The patient in this case was 67 years old and suffered from a variety of ailments, including Parkinson's disease, arthritis, heart disease, a speech impediment, and a history of alcoholism. Four days after his arrival at the nursing home, the patient tried to leave. The employees stopped him, and went so far as to lock up his suitcase and clothes and restrict his access to visitors and the telephone. The patient then tried to walk off the grounds, and the employees responded first by placing him in a wing inhabited by severely emotionally disturbed patients, and then by tying him to a chair. Three weeks later, he finally escaped. He sued, and the court found the nursing home liable. The court stated that the patient had never been declared incompetent and, therefore, had a right to decide to leave.

The only occasions where you can forcibly prevent a patient from leaving is if the patient poses a threat to himself or others. Examples include psychiatric patients, prisoners, patients with a history of violence, and patients with a communicable disease. If you are caring for one of these patients, and the patient threatens to leave, notify your nursing supervisor or the hospital administrator at once.

NON-RESUSCITATION ORDERS

When a patient is terminally ill, the doctor, the patient, and the family may come to an agreement that the patient should not be resuscitated if he or she arrests. The doctor will then write the order on the patient's chart as a "no code" or a "do not resuscitate." You can rest assured that this is a legal order, and you will not be liable when you do not resuscitate the patient.

A problem occurs, however, when the order is not written. Too many times the doctor will simply tell the nursing staff not to resuscitate a particular patient, but then never writes the order. Often, too, the nurses do not document the order anywhere but on the nursing care plan. Be aware that following such an order under these circumstances could place you in a serious legal predicament. If a "no code" order is not written and signed by the doctor, and you fail to initiate resuscitation efforts and the patient dies, then you could be charged with manslaughter or murder. Granted, this is the worse case scenario, but, then again, this is a very serious situation.

If a doctor gives you an order to not resuscitate a patient, write it down on the order sheet and make sure that the doctor signs it. Otherwise, do not honor the order. If you do not have a written and signed order, and the patient arrests, you have an obligation to initiate resuscitation efforts. It is as simple as that.

And, as far as "slow code" orders go, know that these are illegal. The patient should either be resuscitated fully, or the patient should have a written "no code" order and not be resuscitated at all. Participating in a "slow code" could place you at serious legal risk. It is understandable that resuscitating a terminal patient who has been in extreme pain can be emotionally trying and may run counter to your ethical beliefs. However, without a written and signed "no code" order, you have no choice. The only alternative is to try and foresee the occurrence of the situation and talk to the patient's doctor about writing an order not to resuscitate.

Sometimes, a doctor may order a "slow code" in the belief that the patient should not be resuscitated, but the matter has not been presented to the patient's family. Or, it may seem more humane to do something, rather than nothing at all, when the patient arrests. But, again, you need to know that a decision not to resuscitate belongs to the patient or, if incapacitated, to the family or guardian. The doctor must talk with the patient or the family about any order not to resuscitate. The doctor should then document both the conversation about the "no code" order, as well as the process leading to the order, such as the patient's condition and prognosis.

On the other hand, what if the doctor writes a "no code" order that you think is premature? If this occurs, then you have a legal responsibility to question the order. First, document in your nursing notes your reason for questioning the order. For example, if you have made a nursing diagnosis that you think would contradict the appropriateness of a "no code" order, record that. Then, talk with the patient's doctor about your misgivings and ask for clarification for writing the order. After the explanation, you may feel differently. If so, that is fine. But if you do not, or if the doctor will not discuss it with you, then you must document the doctor's response on the medical record and then pursue the matter with higher authorities. Start with your head nurse, but be prepared to follow the channels of hospital authority up to the level of hospital administrator. In the meantime, if the patient arrests before you are satisfied that the order is appropriate, you may initiate resuscitation efforts. Although the situation may be uncomfortable for you, it would be worse to allow a patient to die prematurely and then to find yourself in the middle of a lawsuit. Remember, though, through all of this, that a dying patient has a right to care, dignity, and self-determination which includes a right not to be resuscitated.

PATIENT SELF DETERMINATION ACT

In November of 1991 a federal law went into effect that expands the rights of patients to make critical decisions relative to the health care they receive. The law is called the Patient Self Determination Act of 1991. This Act requires hospitals, nursing homes, home health agencies, hospices, and other institutional Medicare and Medicaid providers to give patients, at the time of their admission, written information concerning their rights under state laws to accept or refuse medical care and to formulate advance directives, which include Living Wills or Durable Powers of Attorney of Health Care. The Patient Self Determination Act also requires that patients be advised of the facility's policy on implementing advance directives. Health care providers must now also document in the patient's medical record whether or not the patient has signed an advance directive. Clearly stated in the law is also the provision that care must not be compromised or refused if a patient has an advance directive. The mandate for community and staff education is also part of this law, though the specifics regarding such education are unclear.

The JCAHO has also mandated that nursing be represented on the institution's ethics committee. This mandate and the importance given to eth-

ical decision making because of the Patient Self Determination Act should help health care organizations recognize the importance of enhanced communication and education between patients and health care providers. This function often has been performed by nurses who were given little support for the activity. Of even greater concern were those patients or families of patients who requested information about their rights to terminate life support and were essentially advised that those decisions were to be left in the hands of the physician. With the new federal law and with its individual state interpretations, this type of response to patients and their families is now illegal. Ensuring that patients' rights to make end-of-life decisions are protected is every nurse's responsibility.

What is a Living Will?

A living will generally states the kind of medical care you want (or do not want) if you become unable to make your own decision. It is called a living will because it takes effect while you are still living. Most states have their own living will forms, each somewhat different. It may also be possible to complete and sign a standard living will form available in your own community, draw up your own form, or simply write a statement of your preferences for treatment.

What is a Durable Power of Attorney for Health Care?

In many states a Durable Power of Attorney for Health Care is a signed, dated, and witnessed paper naming another person, such as a husband, wife, daughter, son, or close friend as your "agent" or "proxy" to make medical decisions for you if you should become unable to make them for yourself. You can include instructions about any treatment you may want or wish to avoid, such as surgery or artificial feeding.

What if you are caring for a patient who has a living will and who has a change of mind, and wants to continue treatment? Then you should consider the will revoked and notify the patient's doctor and your supervisor of the patient's decision. Then, document the patient's statement in the medical record.

Some patients may not have considered a living will until after they have been diagnosed as having a terminal illness. In this instance, you may be the one the patient talks to. If a patient tells you that he or she does not want any extraordinary efforts to be taken to prolong life, have the patient be as specific as possible. Then record the patient's wishes in the medical record, using exact words if possible. It is also a good idea to mention the exact circumstances surrounding the patient's statements. For example, had the patient just been informed about the disease? Had there been a fight with a family member? Or was the patient sitting quietly in bed, calmly talking about the future? But, even in states that have living will laws, a patient's verbal will is not legally binding.

It is important to point out that there is a difference between the patient's right to refuse treatment and the patient's directives in a living will. A patient can always refuse treatment, and, as long as he is competent and meets the other criteria discussed earlier, those wishes must be honored. On the other hand, the directives outlined in a living will do not become effective until after the patient is comatose and no hope for recovery exists.

PATIENT'S ACCESS TO MEDICAL RECORDS

On occasion, you may encounter a patient who demands to read his or her medical record. What should you do? Does the patient have a right to see it? Yes. New laws addressing a patient's rights relative to their medical records were released late in 2000 under the Health Insurance Portability and Accountability Act (HIPAA).

While the record itself belongs to the hospital, the information contained in the record belongs to the patient. The courts have stated that the patient has a right to know details of medical treatment; and, because the patient is paying for the treatment, a right to the information contained in hospital records. The only time that a doctor can legally prevent a patient from reading records is if the record contains information that may actually harm the patient. In this situation, the parties may be able to reach a compromise by allowing a relative of the patient to read the record, instead. Of course, the patient must give approval for this.

If the patient has a right to read the hospital record, then why do many hospitals try to prevent it? The reasons vary. Some consider that the technical language and abbreviations used in the record may produce confusion and anxiety. Others feel that allowing patients to read their own records will encourage medical malpractice lawsuits.

On the positive side, reading the record may help patients better understand their condition and its treatment. It may also be reassuring that no information is being withheld.

If a patient asks you for the chart, first try to determine why. The reason may be a simple one, such as a breakdown in communication, causing the patient to feel inadequately informed. If so, perhaps you can remedy the situation by spending some time with the patient, discussing concerns and answering questions.

If the patient is insistent, notify your nursing supervisor. Even though the patient has a right to read the chart, some hospitals still have requirements that first must be met. For example, some hospitals require patients to make their request through a lawyer. The purpose of this requirement may be to discourage the patient from pursuing the matter.

If the patient gets approval, remain present during the review. Explain any abbreviations and clarify the technical terms. Answer questions as best you can, and encourage the patient to write down any questions for review with the doctor. While the patient has the record, emphasize that, according to state law, it is not allowed to erase or change anything in the record, even if it seems in error.

PATIENT'S RIGHT TO PRIVACY

Through your work as a nurse, you often learn a great deal of very personal information about patients. Insurance companies, the news media, and other health care workers may occasionally ask you to divulge this information, but you have an obligation not to, unless the patient has specifically authorized otherwise.

The patient's right to privacy is firmly grounded both in state laws and in several of the constitutional amendments. What this right means is that no confidential information about the patient will be released without the patient's permission. The courts feel strongly about this right and have gone so far as to declare that protecting a patient's privacy is a doctor's legal duty.

Although most of the privacy laws pertain to the doctor-patient relationship, you have an ethical as well as professional responsibility to protect the patient's rights. The first step to protect these rights is in understanding them.

One of the cases that established a patient's right to privacy occurred in 1920. In this case—*Feeney v. Young* (1920)—the patient had given permission for a film to be made of her Cesarean section with the understanding that it would be shown only for medical purposes. However, the doctor made a film entitled *Birth*, in which scenes of the Cesarean section were incorporated. Subsequently the film was released for viewing by the general public. The patient sued and was awarded damages on the grounds that her privacy had been invaded.

Taking pictures of a patient without consent is the single largest cause of invasion of privacy lawsuits. One such case occurred in 1930, in the case of *Bazemore v. Savannah* (1930). This lawsuit involved a child who had been born with his heart on the outside of his body. The child later died, but not before the hospital allowed a photographer to take a picture of the child. The photographer gave the picture to a newspaper, who then published it. The parents sued the hospital for invasion of privacy and won.

A more recent example concerning the violation of a patient's right to privacy concerned a patient who had cancer of the larynx. Throughout the patient's treatment, the surgeon took numerous photographs. On the day the patient died, the patient made it clear that no more pictures could be taken. However, the doctor ignored the patient's request, even lifting the patient's head on a pillow before taking more pictures. The court later declared that the doctor could be held liable for invasion of privacy.

The patient's right to privacy also carries over to prohibit any unauthorized hospital personnel from observing the patient without permission. This includes student nurses. The only personnel who are legally allowed to observe the patient are those who are directly involved in his or her care. The patient may also sue any unauthorized person who discloses confidential medical information. This includes disclosing information to the media, such as in a case involving a senile 78-year-old man.

Mr. Spring was a patient in a nursing home where he was receiving kidney dialysis treatments. The patient's wife and son (his legal guardians) had been seeking a court order to have Mr. Spring's dialysis treatments discontinued. Without obtaining consent from Mr. Spring's wife or son, the nursing home allowed right-to-life advocates to interview the patient. The advocates then published a story about the situation, which aroused the interest of other reporters. Four nurses at the nursing home later talked with some of those reporters, telling them that Mr. Spring had told them that he did not want to die.

Mrs. Spring and her son eventually obtained the court's permission to make the decision to stop Mr. Spring's dialysis treatments. Mrs. Spring then sued the nursing home and the four nurses who had talked with the reporters, alleging that her husband's privacy had been invaded. The defense attorney argued that the patient had become a "public figure," which would have allowed the disclosure of the information. The jury disagreed, and awarded Mrs. Spring $2.5 million. This amount was later reduced to $100,000 by the Superior Court.

If the patient does not seem to be aware of this right, inform them. For example, explain that permission does not have to be granted to photograph the disorder or its treatment. Information about a patient's condition can be kept from family members at the patient's request.

There are occasions, though, where the courts will permit you to release confidential information. This may occur if the welfare of the patient is at stake. For example, say that the patient has been diagnosed as having brittle diabetes, and frequently suffers from severe hypoglycemia. The patient has instructed you not to tell family about the illness, but you are concerned that the patient's health could be jeopardized if the family is not aware of how to respond if the patient should suffer a hypoglycemia episode. If this occurs, tell the doctor, who can then decide whether to inform the patient's family.

The courts have also ruled that you have a responsibility to disclose information concerning child abuse or neglect, communicable diseases, and gunshot wounds. Courts have also ruled in the past that medical information must be released, despite the patient's objection, when it involves a decision concerning the custody of a child. The court made such a ruling in the case of *D. v. D* (1969). In this case, the mother had a history of illness, and the court wanted a private party to examine the mother's medical records to help determine which parent was most fit to care for the children.

Courts have also determined that a doctor has a right to disclose information when another person's well-being is threatened. For example, in *Tarasoff v. Regents of the University of California* (1976), a patient told a psychotherapist of a plan to kill a particular person. The doctor did not disclose the information, and the patient murdered the person. The parents of the deceased sued the doctor, alleging a responsibility to warn their daughter. The Supreme Court agreed and found the doctor liable for failure to avert the danger.

As you can see, even when the law allows some disclosure, the disclosure is limited. The patient's right to privacy is very real, and you must do your best to uphold it.

EXAM QUESTIONS

CHAPTER 6
Questions 63–77

63. A health care provider could be found guilty of fraudulent concealment by

    a. withholding information to try to cover up a mistake.

    b. concealing the fact that other patients in the hospital have the same illness.

    c. not telling the patient if the hospital's credentials are being evaluated.

    d. hiding from the patient when the patient is in need.

64. What is the meaning of an informed consent?

    a. The patient has consented to a procedure.

    b. The patient has been told when the procedure is scheduled.

    c. The patient has been given a consent form to read and sign.

    d. The patient has been given all the information needed to make a decision regarding treatment.

65. Who is responsible for obtaining the patient's informed consent?

    a. the doctor

    b. the nurse

    c. the hospital administrator

    d. the nursing supervisor

66. If you are about to administer a preoperative medication, and the patient asks you a question that leads you to believe that the patient does not understand the procedure, what should you do?

    a. Give the medication anyway, because the consent is signed and the surgeon is waiting.

    b. Give the medication, but document the patient's questions.

    c. Try to answer the patient's questions and then give the medication.

    d. Hold the medication and call the patient's doctor to come and talk with the patient.

67. If a patient demands information from you about a treatment, you should

    a. ignore the request, because only the doctor can inform.

    b. call the doctor, but avoid telling the patient anything yourself.

    c. evaluate the situation, and decide whether you or the doctor should talk with the patient.

    d. tell the patient whatever he or she wants to know.

68. For the patient to be able to exercise the right to refuse treatment, which of the following criteria must be satisfied?

    a. The condition cannot be life-threatening.

    b. The patient's immediate family must agree with the patient's decision.

    c. The patient must be mentally competent and aware of both condition and prognosis.

    d. The patient must be terminal with no hope for survival.

69. When would an informed consent not be necessary?

    a. if the patient has waived the right to have one

    b. if the patient does not speak English

    c. if the patient is a minor

    d. if the procedure isn't life-threatening

70. If a nurse or a doctor continues treatment after the patient has refused, which of the following could result?

    a. The health care provider would be free from liability as long as the patient's family approved.

    b. The health care provider would be free from liability as long as the treatment was successful.

    c. The patient could sue the health care provider for battery.

    d. The patient could sue the health care provider for malpractice, but only if the procedure was not successful.

71. Consider that the patient you are caring for has refused a blood transfusion based on religious beliefs. In which instance would the court most likely override the patient's request?

    a. if the patient was a Jehovah's Witness

    b. if the patient was a mother of two children

    c. if the patient was a single male about to be married

    d. if the patient was critically ill

72. In which situation can a health care provider legally fail to resuscitate a patient?

    a. when the patient is terminal

    b. when the patient's family requests you not to

    c. when the doctor verbally says not to resuscitate if the patient arrests

    d. when the patient's chart contains a written "no code" order

73. If a patient is comatose for a long period of time, who is qualified to give consent?

    a. the patient's caretaker

    b. the patient's doctor

    c. the patient's child

    d. the patient's court-appointed guardian

74. When does a living will become effective?

    a. as soon as a patient decides to invoke it

    b. when the patient's family decides to invoke it

    c. as soon as the patient is diagnosed as having a terminal illness

    d. when a terminally ill patient is comatose and has no reasonable chance for recovery

75. If a patient demands to see the hospital chart, your immediate response should be to

    a. refuse; the patient has no right to read it.

    b. sedate the patient and then notify your supervisor.

    c. try to determine why the patient wants to see the chart and try to answer any questions.

    d. contact the hospital's legal department.

76. Which of the following situations could trigger a patient's lawsuit for invasion of privacy?

    a. if the patient has not been given a private room after one was requested

    b. if the patient's nurse asks for the patient's birthdate

    c. if someone takes a picture of the patient without consent

    d. if the patient's nurse sees the patient naked

77. The court may allow you to release confidential information about a patient if

    a. the patient is terminal.

    b. the patient has a unique disease.

    c. the patient's welfare is at stake.

    d. the patient's family requests the information.

CHAPTER 7

KNOWING WHAT TO EXPECT IF YOU ARE NAMED IN A LAWSUIT

CHAPTER OBJECTIVE

After studying this chapter, the reader will be able to describe the usual progression of a medical malpractice lawsuit, from the filing of the complaint through the trial.

LEARNING OBJECTIVES

After reading this chapter, the reader will be able to

1. identify three pieces of information that can be learned from reading a patient's complaint.

2. describe three situations in which the statute of limitations for filing a lawsuit may be extended.

3. identify the first action one should take upon being served with a complaint.

4. describe what occurs during the period of discovery, and identify the usual length of this period.

5. list three tools lawyers use to obtain information during discovery.

6. identify four purposes for taking someone's deposition.

7. specify four activities that a lawyer may ask a client to perform to prepare for a deposition.

8. list six general guidelines to follow when answering questions on a deposition.

9. state the usual reason for settling a malpractice lawsuit before trial.

10. list four general guidelines to follow when testifying at trial.

11. identify the function of the expert witness.

12. define the parties who participate in an arbitration process.

Even if you try your best to maintain appropriate standards of care, you may still find yourself being named in a lawsuit. Even if you do not feel you were negligent, you may still be sued. Just because you do not feel you have done anything to contribute to a patient's injury won't necessarily prevent a patient from naming you in a lawsuit.

Hopefully, the day will never come when you find out you have been personally named in a medical malpractice lawsuit. But if it does, you need to know what to expect.

RECEIVING NOTICE OF THE LAWSUIT

The first notice you will probably receive that you are being sued is when you receive a copy of the summons and complaint. The complaint is the official document in which the patient outlines grievances against you and perhaps several other members of the health care team. The summons lets you know how many days you have in which to respond officially to the patient's charges. The summons may also specify the damages being sought.

To serve you with the complaint, a member of the sheriff's office or some other representative of the plaintiff will most likely approach you and ask your name. When you respond by affirming your name, the representative will simply hand you the complaint. It is as simple as that. At that point, the court will consider you officially "served."

When you first look at the complaint, you may or may not recognize the name of one of your former patients listed at the top of the document above the title of "plaintiff." Members of the patient's family may join in the lawsuit. Below the plaintiffs, the document will list the defendants, or the persons being sued. Besides your name, other members of the health care team—including the patient's doctor, other nurses, your supervisor, and the hospital—may also be listed.

As you read further, you will learn that the patient is accusing you of having been negligent and is also claiming injury as a result. Keep in mind that the complaint—although it must list the four elements required to prove malpractice, which are duty, breach of duty or negligence, causation of an injury, and damages—is intentionally vague. You will not find any details here about the patient's treatment. That is because, at this point in a lawsuit, the plaintiff's attorney may hope to discover other, more specific, claims of negligence as the case is investigated further. Also, do not panic when you read the amount which is being claimed as damages. As this point in the suit, the amount generally has little resemblance to what will ultimately be paid.

STATUTE OF LIMITATIONS

Do not panic if you do not recognize the plaintiff's name. After all, in most instances, the patient has anywhere from six months to three years (depending upon the state) from the date of the alleged occurrence of malpractice to file a lawsuit. This is what is known as the statute of limitations.

In fact, the statute of limitations may extend even further, depending upon whether certain circumstances exist. One such instance is if the patient did not know that someone caring for him or her had been negligent. For example, imagine that a female patient had been visiting her doctor for unexplained vaginal bleeding. The doctor recommended a hysterectomy. The patient agreed, but specified that she did not want her ovaries removed. The doctor agreed that, yes, he felt that would be the best course. However, during the course of surgery, the doctor inadvertently removed the patient's ovaries. After the surgery, he did not tell her that he had done so, and did not prescribe necessary hormonal therapy. Two years pass, during which the patient has complained to the doctor of a variety of symptoms that could have been relieved by hormonal therapy, but the doctor did nothing. Finally, the patient visits another doctor and discovers after a diagnostic work-up that her first doctor had removed her ovaries without her consent and that he had not been treating the resultant hormonal deficiency. It is at this point that the time the patient has for filing a lawsuit starts to run. State law dictates how long the patient can wait before filing a lawsuit after discovering the error, but the usual time allowed ranges from one to three years.

Another instance in which the statute of limitations may be prolonged is if the patient's injury resulted from a series of treatments rather than from a single incident. An example of this might be if a patient claimed to have been burned during a series of radiation therapy treatments. In this type of situation, the statute of limitations would begin to run as of the date of the last treatment.

Also, if the alleged act of malpractice affected a minor, the amount of time allowed for filing a lawsuit varies even more. Some states do not begin to apply the statute of limitations until the minor has reached the age of majority, which ranges from 18 to 21 years, depending upon the state.

As you can see, it may have been years since you have taken care of this patient who has just accused you of being negligent. Even if you do not remember the patient, and cannot imagine how you could have been negligent, stay calm. At this point, there is nothing you can do about the lawsuit. You have been named and served. Now it is up to you to keep your cool and work with an attorney to develop the best defense possible.

THE FIRST STEP

The first thing you need to do is notify the hospital risk manager or in-house counsel of the receipt of the summons and complaint. If you carry your own insurance, you should also notify your insurance company of the lawsuit. Check your policy for instructions on whom to notify. Either way, it is important that you contact all the appropriate people immediately. If you delay and do not notify your insurance company within a certain period time, they can refuse to cover you at all. For this reason, it is best to notify them by certified mail with a return receipt requested. That way, you have documentation that you notified your company on time.

Whatever you do, though, do not attempt to contact the plaintiff or the plaintiff's attorney to talk about the situation or to drop the lawsuit. Not only will this probably not work, everything you say to the plaintiff could come back to haunt you in court. A jury could very well interpret your actions to mean that you were not confident enough about your innocence to handle the lawsuit through proper channels.

Once you have notified your employer and your insurance company, your insurance company will hire a lawyer to defend you. If you are insured under your employer's policy or your own independent policy, the insurance company will provide legal counsel. If you do not have any insurance, you will have to hire your own lawyer. Granted, this can be very expensive, but this is one instance when you will not be able to go it alone. Medical malpractice lawsuits are extremely complicated, and you will need professional help to defend yourself.

The first job your lawyer will perform will be to immediately file a response—called the answer—to the plaintiff's complaint, in which your innocence will be asserted. Next, your attorney will learn as much as possible about the situation that stimulated the lawsuit. This phase of investigation is officially known as discovery.

THE PROCESS OF DISCOVERY

Discovery is the period of time the lawyers for both the plaintiffs and the defendants try to learn as much as they can about the case. This includes investigating the plaintiff's medical care and treatment, the costs associated with that care, current medical condition, prognosis, and past medical history. If the plaintiff is claiming inability to work because of injury, the lawyers will investigate whether this is true by talking with the plaintiff's past and present employers and verifying past and present earnings. The lawyers will also want to find out as much about you and the other defendants as possible, including your education and experience as well as your employment history.

All of this investigation can take from several months to several years, depending upon the number of parties involved, the complexity of the case and the court in which the case is filed. Many malpractice cases go to trial within three years of the date the lawsuit was filed; however, in urban areas where cases are backlogged, many cases may not reach trial for 10 to 12 years after the initial filing of the summons and complaint.

Throughout the long and tedious process of discovery, always cooperate with your lawyer. If your insurance company has provided you with a lawyer, and you do not cooperate, the insurance company could refuse to cover you. And, if they do, you could be forced to find, and pay for, a lawyer of your own. But this does not mean that you are completely at your lawyer's mercy. For example, if you do not feel that your lawyer is acting in your best interest, speak up. Tell both the lawyer and your insurance company representative.

As part of the investigative process, your lawyer will want to hear your version of the incident. Before this first consultation, request a copy of all pertinent hospital records so that you can accurately reconstruct the incident as it occurred. When you tell your side of the story, be as honest as you can. Do not twist the truth to make yourself look better. Remember that your lawyer's job is to defend you, so you need to give him as much honest information as you can. If you know you made a mistake, admit it. Whatever you tell your lawyer is privileged; that information cannot be shared with anyone without your permission.

Throughout the period of discovery, the lawyers use a variety of techniques to obtain information. One way of obtaining basic information is through the filing of what are known as interrogatories. Interrogatories are simply written questions addressed to the other party, which that other party is required to answer within a certain amount of time. The plaintiff will no doubt serve you with interrogatories, and you will need to answer them promptly. The questions typically ask for personal information—such as your age and address—professional information—such as where you went to school, where you have worked, and whether you have received any advanced training—and, of course, information about the incident in question. Once you have answered the questions as best you can, your lawyer will take your answers and draft them into a legal document and return to the plaintiff's attorney. Review relevant medical records carefully prior to answering interrogatories. Do not answer a question unless you are certain of the correct answer.

Another method of obtaining information is through a request for production of documents. Again, this is a legal document which asks the other party to produce certain documents pertinent to the case. For example, your lawyer will ask the plaintiff for copies of medical bills, evidence of any salary lost because of the injury, photographs of the injury, and a copy of the medical records. In turn, the plaintiff's attorney will no doubt request a copy of all relevant medical records, copies of your employer's policies and procedures, standards of care, personnel files, patient acuity logs, and staffing records.

But perhaps one of the most important techniques used for discovering information is the deposition.

DEPOSITIONS

In a deposition, a lawyer for one party asks questions of the opposing party in front of a court reporter while the party being questioned is under oath. After the lawyers take the depositions of all of the parties in the lawsuit, they will take the depositions of witnesses. Witnesses may include people who actually witnessed the alleged act of malpractice, people who know about the incident, health care providers who have cared for the plaintiff before and since the incident, expert witnesses, and family and friends of the plaintiff. The plaintiff's family and friends usually testify as to how the plaintiff's life has changed since the injury.

Taking a deposition allows the lawyers to talk with the actual parties involved in the lawsuit and to find out what their testimony will be at trial. Many times, lawyers can learn about other witnesses through taking someone's deposition. A deposition transcript can be read at trial when a certain witness cannot appear and testify in person. A lawyer may use a deposition to help refresh the memory of a witness, or to point out changes in the witness' testimony between the deposition and the trial. This latter technique would help the lawyer discredit the character of the witness.

Depositions also allow the lawyers to evaluate how effective a certain witness will be at trial. For example, a witness' appearance, demeanor, and believability are often more important than what the witness says and may alter the outcome of a trial. It is the information learned during depositions that can determine whether or not the plaintiff's lawyer proceeds with a case or whether your lawyer tries to settle the case before trial.

Before the plaintiff's lawyer takes your deposition, you will meet with your lawyer to review the case. Your lawyer will probably ask you to read through the plaintiff's entire medical record—including order sheets, operative notes, and laboratory reports—to refamiliarize yourself with the plaintiff's care and medical history. This is very important. Remember, the court holds you accountable for being aware of information contained in the entire medical record. If the plaintiff's lawyer can point out to the jury that you were unaware of certain aspects of the plaintiff's medical history or care, it could be successfully inferred that you must have been giving less than adequate care.

While you are reviewing the plaintiff's medical record, jot down notes or any questions. But remember, never write on the record itself, and do not try and make any corrections. The time for correcting anything inaccurate in the record is long passed, and doing so now could make it look as if you were trying to cover something up. If you notice an inconsistency or an inaccuracy in the record, make a note of it and mention it to your lawyer.

Your lawyer may also ask you to read articles or books that are pertinent to the case, or to read the deposition transcripts of other witnesses, including the expert witnesses who will be called to testify against you. To stimulate recall of the facts, your lawyer may also arrange to meet with you and the other defendants in the case at the same time. This can be effective; however, keep in mind that you should only do this if your lawyer is present. If your lawyer is not present, the court will assume that these conversations were not part of trial preparation, and the plaintiff's lawyer will have a right to discover not only with whom you talked, but what each party said. For this reason, you will want to limit what you say to anyone about the lawsuit.

When it's time for you to actually be deposed, you will go either to the office of one of the lawyers or to a room in the courthouse. Your lawyer will be there, and so will the lawyers of all of the other parties in the lawsuit. Remember that each defendant in the lawsuit may have his or her own lawyer. If the plaintiff's doctor is being sued along with you, the doctor may also have a lawyer or you may share lawyers. However, the hospital's insurance company may appoint a separate lawyer to represent each party if it appears that a common defense cannot be offered.

Regardless, you and the co-defendants must realize that, just because you are both defendants in the lawsuit, you are not necessarily allies. The lawyer for a co-defendant may try to defend a client best by blaming you.

Besides the lawyers, a court reporter will be present to record everything that is said. Although the atmosphere at a deposition may be more casual than the atmosphere at trial, the testimony given during a deposition is no less vital. The transcript of a deposition is an official record of a party's or a witness' testimony taken while under oath, and a portion, or all, of that transcript can be read into the record at trial. Therefore, if you change your testimony between the time you give your deposition and the time you testify at trial, the plaintiff's attorney can use that discrepancy to discredit you in front of the jury.

Once you have taken an oath to tell the truth, the plaintiff's lawyer will begin to ask you questions. On occasion, your lawyer may object to a question. If so, listen carefully to what is said; it may be a clue as to how to answer. Basically, you will answer all questions—unless your lawyer tells you not to—and the judge will rule on your lawyer's objections at trial before admitting your answer into evidence.

When the plaintiff's lawyer has finished asking questions, the lawyers for the other defendants may also ask you questions. Once they have finished, your lawyer may ask you a few questions, especially to clarify something for the record.

But no matter who is asking the questions, do not anticipate what that person is going to ask. Wait until the question is complete, and then provide only the information asked for. Do not volunteer anything. If you can adequately answer a question by simply saying yes or no, then do so. If the lawyer wants more information, ask to have the question broken down. A common tactic lawyers use is to remain silent after the deponent has finished answering, hoping to prod the deponent into giving even more information. Do not fall for it. Be

honest, but do not make the plaintiff's lawyer's job easy by volunteering things not even asked for.

If the lawyer asks you a question that is very broad and that you will have difficulty answering succinctly, ask for a more specific question. Also, watch out for any broad, oversimplified statements with which the lawyer will ask you to agree. Lawyers often try to do this, thinking that if they can get deponents to reach a conclusion about a hypothetical situation, they can then use that conclusion against them in court.

If you do not understand a particular question, or if you think a question is ambiguous, ask the lawyer to rephrase it so that you can be more specific in your answer. Do not be trapped into giving a long narrative answer, during which you may say something that could later be used against you. Never try to guess at an answer about which you are not really sure. Although the lawyer may know that you are guessing and that you do not really know the answer, this will not stop your answer from being presented at trial as if it were a fact. After all, you were under oath.

If you do not know an answer, then say so. A jury will understand that it has been some time since the incident occurred, and that it is only natural to forget some things. You may ask for time to review the medical record if you are certain the answer is in it. Take all the time you need to ensure you are giving a correct response. But the jury will not understand if you exaggerate or lie. If the plaintiff's lawyer can show that you lied about one answer, the jury may be suspicious about all of your other answers and may not believe you at all. But, once you have answered a question, stick with your answer. Changing your answer, or vacillating, can make you appear less than credible.

Another point to remember is that, when you are answering questions, resist the temptation to explain something you do not feel the plaintiff's lawyer understands such as some technical aspect of medicine or a matter of physiology. Again, this only makes the plaintiff's lawyer's job easier. Also, without knowing it, you may be giving information that can be used to win their case.

If the lawsuit involves a situation in which an error obviously occurred—such as in a case where the patient's right leg was amputated instead of his left—do not attempt to dance around the issue. In that situation, it may be better to simply admit that an error occurred. But, if a key point of the lawsuit is whether an error occurred or not, do not let the plaintiff's lawyer lead you into making a statement that a mistake was made. Your lawyer will help you prepare for these more technical aspects of your testimony, but, when you are actually testifying, you will be pretty much on your own. That is why you need to listen carefully to each question, and carefully analyze your answer, before actually speaking.

Something else to keep in mind during your deposition is that a court reporter must record everything that is said. That is why you must always answer questions verbally, not by nodding or shaking your head. You also need to avoid mumbling, or saying "uh-huh" or other such phrases that cannot be easily written down. This is another reason to let the lawyer finish the question before you start to answer; it is impossible for the court reporter to record when two people talk at once.

The court reporter's presence is also a reason why it is important that you make an extra effort to stay calm. Anything you say will be recorded by the court reporter, including a flippant remark or words said in anger. Because the deposition can be read at trial, these statements could give the jury a bad impression of you.

If you are beginning to feel frazzled, ask to take a break. If you are being deposed, you essentially control the deposition, and you can take a break whenever you feel you need one. You may also want to ask for a break if you feel you gave an incorrect answer earlier in your deposition. This way, you can tell your lawyer about it and, if it is necessary, ask you a question to help you clarify the record.

Some time after the deposition, you will receive a copy of the transcript. You should read through it and note any errors the court reporter made when transcribing your testimony. You will be given a sheet which is expressly for noting any such errors. However, you can only note errors made in transcription; you cannot use this as an opportunity to change your testimony. Once you have reviewed the transcript and made any changes, you will sign the correction sheet before a notary public and return it to the reporter or your lawyer.

THE TRIAL

Remember that most malpractice cases never actually reach trial. Lawyers estimate that only about 10% of the medical malpractice cases filed actually go to court. Even then, only about 10% of those end up with a final judgment. The rest are settled out of court or dismissed.

The reasons for settling out of court vary. In general, the lawyer must balance the merits and liabilities of the case along with the expense of prolonged litigation. Cases likely to arouse considerable sympathy (for example, cases where babies or children are injured) are often settled if defense counsel believes a jury will be unable to look past the injury and deny the child any payment. You may have no say as to whether your case is settled; it is often left up to the lawyers and the insurance companies to decide. If your case is settled, do not feel that you have admitted to being negligent. Settling is just a way of reaching a compromise among all sides, and to avoid the emotionally and financially draining process of a prolonged legal battle.

If your case does go to trial, you need to be ready. If your lawyer tells you how to dress and how to act, listen to the advice. After all, your lawyer wants to win the case, too, and, after years of experience, knows how a typical jury will react to a specific type of person. Good general rules to follow are to dress conservatively. The importance of making a good impression on the jury cannot be underestimated. As a defendant, you will be sitting at the defense table with your lawyer, and the jury's eyes may be on you throughout the trial. Be attentive to the testimony being given, and do not make faces or gestures if you disagree with someone's testimony. Try to exude confidence about the trial's outcome.

Before you actually show up at the courthouse, you will want to review the patient's medical record again, your deposition transcript, your interrogatory answers, the deposition transcript of the expert witness offering testimony against you, and any other materials your lawyer suggests. You must have all of the facts straight in your mind before the trial even begins.

On the first day of the trial, the main task will be to select a jury. In some states, though, medical malpractice cases are heard before a judge alone, in which case a jury would not be selected. But, if a jury is to be used, the lawyers representing each of the parties will attempt to select a jury by asking potential jurors certain questions. Lawyers structure their questions so as to learn as much about a potential juror's background, education, and biases. More than anything, a lawyer wants to know whether a specific person will be sympathetic to either client. Each lawyer may reject a certain number of prospective jurors without having to give a reason. For example, a lawyer may just have an intuitive feeling that a particular person may not be sympathetic. Lawyers may reject an unlimited number of jurors for specific reasons. For example, if a potential juror plays golf with the plaintiff every Saturday, then the defense lawyers would

have cause to suspect that that juror would not be impartial.

Once the jury is selected, the trial will begin. The plaintiff's attorney will call witnesses, and present the case first because the burden of proof rests with the plaintiff. Once the plaintiff's case has been presented, the defense will begin, and your lawyer will then call witnesses who will refute the plaintiff's allegations and support you.

Unlike television, trials are not always exciting and fast paced. Instead, they can be painfully slow moving. It may seem to you that the trial is going nowhere because of constant interruptions in the form of recesses and meetings between the lawyers in the judge's chambers where they argue about some point of law. Be patient and try to remain calm. Remember that many of the issues raised in medical malpractice cases are technical and complex. The better everyone—including the judge and all of the lawyers—understands these issues, the more likely that a fair verdict will be rendered.

Realize that when the trial is on recess the jury is also on recess, and they may be watching you. Be careful of how you act and of what you say. If a juror were to overhear you saying something derogatory about the plaintiff, or to see you acting disrespectfully to a court officer, your case could be damaged.

Do not speak with the plaintiff during the breaks, but, if you happen to meet him, say, at the water fountain, be polite. The same thing goes for members of the jury. You should not talk with them, but you are bound to run into them in the elevator, the cafeteria, or the hallway. Again, be polite, but do not engage in conversation.

GIVING YOUR TESTIMONY

When it is time for you to testify, remember that your appearance and your demeanor will be almost as important as what you have to say. It is important that the jury like you, that they feel you are sincere and that you are telling the truth. Pay attention to the questions you are asked and answer simply and in lay terms. Remember, the jury will decide the outcome, and you want them to understand—and believe—your answers.

You will have no doubt prepared for your testimony with your lawyer before the trial, so you should know what your lawyer is going to ask and also have a good idea what the plaintiff's lawyer will ask. More than anything else, preparing adequately is the key to being an effective witness.

When you are called to the witness stand, your lawyer will ask you questions first. This is where the style of your testimony will differ from that of your deposition. On your deposition, you gave short, specific answers, and often answered simply with a yes or a no. But here, with your lawyer asking the questions, you want to open up a bit. Now you have control, and this is your chance to tell your side of the story. Sit up straight in the witness chair, and even lean slightly forward, which shows you're interested. And always talk to the jury. Even though your lawyer's the one asking the questions, look at the jury when you answer. Again, this is your only chance to talk to the jury.

This is also a chance to bring your patient teaching skills into play. While you wanted to avoid teaching the plaintiff's attorney during your deposition, you need to educate the jury. You want them to understand the technical aspects of the case, the pathophysiology of the plaintiff's illness, and the standards of nursing care. If you have access to a visual aid that you think will help the jury understand, talk with your lawyer about it ahead of time. If you both agree that it will be helpful, practice talking and using the aid at home before you come to the courtroom. Once there, make sure that the jury's view will not be blocked

and that every juror can see what you are showing them.

Once your lawyer has finished with the direct examination, the plaintiff's lawyer will cross-examine you. Now is when you need to revert back to the style you used during your deposition. Be alert because, as you know, the plaintiff's attorney will try to discredit your testimony and get you to change an answer you gave in response to one of your lawyer's questions, or an answer you gave during your deposition. The plaintiff's lawyer may also make statements and ask whether you agree or disagree. This attempt is to limit your answers to yes and no; do your best to try and answer in your own words. Otherwise, the plaintiff's lawyer will be doing most of your testifying for you.

Although this aspect of testifying can be frustrating, always be polite and keep calm. Realize that, if necessary, your lawyer can ask additional questions after the plaintiff's attorney is finished. This way, you have a chance to clarify any answers that you feel the jury may have misunderstood because of the plaintiff's lawyer's cross-examination style.

Another thing to remember during the cross-examination is to say, "I do not know," if you honestly do not know. This alone will help your credibility with the jury more than if you try and guess. But beware of saying, "I do not know" about a situation that was obviously exceptional and where the jury would have a hard time believing that you "do not know" or "do not remember." In this situation, your credibility could be damaged, or even destroyed.

One case where a nurse claimed she could not remember, and the jury did not believe her, is *Salas by Salas v. Wang* (1988). In this instance, a woman was admitted to the hospital in active labor. When her obstetrician ruptured her membranes, he noted that the amniotic fluid was meconium stained. The doctor then told the nurse in the delivery room to notify the Intensive Care Nursery (ICN) of the delivery, and to have them send down the ICN team who routinely helped with such high-risk births.

The delivery room nurse called the ICN on three separate occasions during the patient's labor and spoke to the ICN charge nurse. She made the last call at 11:08 p.m., at which time she told the ICN charge nurse to send down the ICN team immediately. Although the ICN team could have arrived within one minute of having received the call, the team did not arrive for 22 minutes, which was three minutes after the baby had been born. The baby suffered severe brain damage and is non-ambulatory and profoundly mentally retarded.

The parents sued the doctor, the hospital, and the nurses, including the ICN charge nurse. The charge nurse stated that she "did not recall" the conversations with the delivery room nurse, although she did not deny that they occurred. However, because the events that took place on this evening should have been memorable, the nurse's claim that she "did not remember" cast doubt on her credibility. The court commented that, because the ICN charge nurse appeared to be concealing her knowledge of the events of that day, the jury could reasonably conclude that it was the charge nurse's negligence that proximately caused the ICN team to fail to arrive in a timely manner. The jury awarded the plaintiffs $6.5 million.

THE EXPERT WITNESS

A key witness in any medical malpractice lawsuit is the expert witness. Besides explaining to the court the appropriate standards of care, the expert witness also pinpoints where the alleged acts of negligence occurred. Because the areas on which medical malpractice cases focus are so technical and complex, the jury often could not make a decision unless someone competent in the field explained in layman's language exactly what was involved.

In most malpractice actions brought against nurses, a nurse expert witness will testify to establish the appropriate standard of care and identify how the nurse did or did not deviate from that standard. It is possible that the plaintiff's attorney will use someone other than a nurse—for example a doctor—to act as an expert witness regarding the nurse's care. This depends upon the state in which you practice. Some states require that the expert have the same background as the defendant. In other words, if the case involves a claim of negligence against an operating room nurse, then the expert witness must be a nurse specializing in that same field.

For the most part, though, the nursing expert witness will be skilled in the same area of nursing the defendant was practicing when the alleged malpractice occurred. Witnesses qualify as expert based on their educational background and their experience. Besides extensive clinical experience, the witness may also have written articles about the area in question, conducted research in that same area, and may also belong to certain technical and professional organizations. The expert witness usually does not have any personal knowledge about the events involved in the case. Instead, the witnesses are hired by either the plaintiff's lawyer or the defendant's lawyer and paid a fee to review the medical records and render an opinion.

Both at trial and in deposition, the nursing expert witness will identify the appropriate standard of care for the situation involved in the lawsuit, then testify as to which specific acts deviated from those standards. Besides experience and knowledge, the expert may review books and publications pertinent to the area to help form an opinion.

REACHING A VERDICT

Once both parties have presented their cases, the lawyers will give their closing arguments. It is here that the lawyers will make their final effort to convince the jury as to how they should vote. The judge will instruct the jury about the points of law they should consider to reach their verdict. After that, the jury will withdraw to review the facts and exhibits of the case. When the jury has come to a unanimous decision as to the verdict, they will return to the courtroom and announce their verdict to all parties. If either lawyer is not satisfied with the verdict feeling the judge did not interpret the law properly or instruct the jury properly, then the lawyer may appeal.

TORT REFORM

Tort Reform Initiatives to Control Liability Risks

In attempting to increase profits through a reduction in the volume of care, however, providers under the current system of managed care will almost certainly be exposed to greater risk of malpractice. In fact, today's liability environment presents a dilemma to providers as it forces them to do more, rather than less, in order to protect themselves against the risk of malpractice. The question for providers is—How can we decrease costs and enhance profits while providing the best possible care for the individual and protect ourselves against litigation?

As the system currently exists, a medical malpractice claim filed for litigation is based on tort law. A tort is a wrongful act or omission (not based on a contract) that causes injury to another person. Tort law provides a framework of compensation for those damages that an injured person incurs as a result of medical malpractice. Most malpractice litigation is based on negligence. The threat of litiga-

tion alone may discourage negligence and other substandard care.

In the courts, recovering damages for negligence is a multistep process. As part of the process, the attorney for the injured person (plaintiff) must establish, usually through expert witness testimony, the standard of care to which the health care provider is accountable. Furthermore, the attorney must also prove that the provider failed to meet this standard and subsequently caused an injury resulting in damage or loss. If a plaintiff proves that the provider's negligence or fault caused this injury, the plaintiff is entitled to recover damages. The uncertainty associated with how a judge or jury may decide a claim often affects plaintiffs', providers', and insurers' decisions in making a settlement versus going to trial. In fact, most claims are withdrawn or settled before the case reaches a verdict.

During the mid-70s, malpractice insurance costs increased rapidly, partly because of an increase in the number of claims filed along with the size of settlements and awards. As a result, insurance became unaffordable or unavailable for many health care providers, thus creating a medical malpractice crisis. Almost all states responded to the crisis by changing tort laws to reduce the amount of litigation and damages paid. Some enacted legislation in order to allow alternatives to litigation.

Over the past two decades, much attention has been devoted to an attempt to strike a balance between patients' rights and the protection of health care providers. These attempts, however, have come from a civil justice system thought to be unpredictable, inefficient, and expensive. To date, despite repeated attempts at tort reform, no satisfactory solution has been achieved.

Providers and insurers feel the tort system adds to health costs without effectively deterring malpractice or compensating medical injury victims. They also feel that the current tort system has some broad negative effects on the overall health care system:

- It can adversely affect the provider-patient relationship.

- It can deter providers from offering high-risk procedures in order to avoid exposure to malpractice allegations.

- It can encourage the practice of defensive medicine.

The legal profession, on the other hand, feels that tort reform does not adequately address the issues at hand. Professional liability is a tiny piece of overall health costs, the trial lawyers contend, and any discussion of tort reform merely serves as a mask for medicine's true agenda; that is, avoiding responsibility for negligence. To support their position, they point out that:

- Adverse events due to negligent practice rarely result in a lawsuit (only 2% of such events lead to malpractice claims).

- Juries are not systematically biased against providers (malpractice defendants win more than 65% of cases, a better record than defendants in other kinds of personal injury cases).

- Juries decide cases on the basis of the provider's quality of care rather than the patient's severity of injury.

With such a polarization of viewpoints, one wonders whether any middle ground can be achieved. In the debate over reforming the U.S. health care system, however, one area of near universal agreement was the need to reform the nation's medical malpractice system. Since health care is evolving into a managed care economy, an examination of existing and proposed reforms; no-fault, enterprise liability, enterprise no-fault, the private contract, and arbitration may shed some light on the direction the future will take.

No-Fault Liability

No-fault programs are designed to remove the difficulty of proving that an injury resulted from a health care provider's negligence or fault. Generally, under the no-fault alternative, compensable injuries and compensation amounts are specified. After an injury has been established, it is not necessary to identify the cause.

Malpractice reforms have been enacted in Florida (1989) and Virginia (1988) that only apply to claims involving infants with neurological injuries at birth. Both states have enacted no-fault funds that pay set amounts to the injured party.

In both programs, physicians voluntarily choose to participate and pay an annual fee to a state fund. About 75% of the obstetricians and gynecologists in both states participate. In Virginia, about 51% of the state's hospitals are in the program and pay for each delivery up to a maximum of $150,000 per year. In Florida, all private hospitals are taxed to help fund the program, but public and teaching hospitals are exempt. About 50% of Florida's hospitals are private and are assessed for each delivery with no maximum annual limit.

The Florida and Virginia programs have had some success. For example, one of Virginia's largest malpractice insurers resumed writing policies for obstetrical coverage as a result of this program. Fewer claims than expected have been filed; however, program officials suggest several reasons for this, including the fact that the time from injury to claim filing typically takes several years for the type of injury these programs target.

Enterprise Liability

One of the most controversial proposed reforms aimed at the managed care environment is enterprise liability. As initially envisioned, it was to shift liability from individual providers to the enterprise at which they practiced. The authors saw those generally as hospitals, but federal reformers switched the focus to the accountable health plans that would provide insurance coverage in managed competition.

In theory, enterprise liability is an attempt to marry liability and quality assurance at the plan level. The authors feel it improves quality by placing liability squarely on the enterprises that control health care delivery and, accordingly, can take steps to reduce patient injuries. It also appears to be a good fit with the total quality improvement concepts, which have taken hold in American health care in recent years. By making the entities that control quality liable for medical injuries, overall quality will be improved. Peer review is more effective than licensing boards and the current tort system.

Additionally, enterprise liability provides cost savings, not only by reducing the number of injuries, but also by eliminating the administrative duplication that now exists. A single defense provided to the enterprise would be less expensive than the overlapping and sometimes conflicting array of attorneys that now represent the various parties in a malpractice lawsuit. Removing physicians from the system would also eliminate their motivation to practice defensive medicine.

Health care reformers saw enterprise liability as solving the decades-old reform war fought by physicians and attorneys in state legislatures. By removing the legal threat from health care providers and leaving malpractice plaintiffs' attorneys untouched, they viewed enterprise liability as a masterstroke of accommodation. What they did not calculate was the opposition from just about everyone that had a stake in health care reform.

Consumer groups want errant health care providers held directly accountable for their own negligence. They feel the process of enterprise liability is a step toward a no fault system for medical malpractice.

Hospitals are adamantly opposed to being saddled with billions of dollars in additional liability, thus opening the door to passing such costs on to physicians through surcharges. They will be unlikely to base liability surcharges on individual provider risks and instead, would be far more likely to add up the total cost of additional liability and divide it among the medical staff.

Professional liability insurers see their very existence threatened. They are of the opinion that enterprise liability would result in higher awards and more lawsuits since it would be much easier to bring a meritless claim against big business than against your family physician. Health insurers who hope to administer managed care plans do not want to be the focus of liability pressure or defendants in malpractice cases.

Enterprise No Fault

Many favor a shift from the present fault-based system of liability to a broader system of strict liability imposed on the hospital or other health care organization for all medical injuries, whether or not carelessness is demonstrated. This would be accomplished by experience rating institutions' and organizations' insurance premiums. Every organization would then be provided a powerful incentive not only to monitor itself for the carelessness or ignorance that underlies negligence, but also to mount prevention programs directed at all negligent and non-negligent injuries.

Although the size of financial awards would be smaller than under the current open-ended manner of tort damages, payment would be the responsibility of the provider organization within which the substandard care took place. This would contrast with the present arrangement where legal payments are displaced into non-merit rated malpractice insurance that raises the premiums of all physicians in a particular area because of the actions of some of their colleagues.

The proposal would also considerably expand liability from the tiny fraction of negligently injured patients who now receive payments for a tort claim. The reason is that patients would find it much easier to show medical causation rather than to prove physician negligence. Furthermore, as higher numbers of compensable accidents filter into the system, medical care organizations would have increased incentive to look for patterns of injury causes. These organizations would likely monitor more closely the practice patterns and privileges of those physicians who are more accident prone.

Compensation under this proposal would focus on the tangible financial losses of all injured patients. Rather than serve as first dollar primary insurance for all the financial losses of a handful of successful tort claimants, liability dollars would be concentrated on those who suffer long-term injuries and are not protected against catastrophic losses by other sources of medical and disability insurance. Payment would be made on a set scale similar to no-fault workers' compensation benefits. Contestable cases would be few and would be handled in a forum analogous to state workers' compensation boards.

The enterprise no-fault theory received little or no support from any of the parties involved in reform even though it contained several plausible arguments. Physicians, medical care organizations, and insurers that opposed enterprise liability quickly dismissed the underlying principles of this treatise. Much stronger, however, was the opposition from trial attorneys who adamantly opposed any effort to turn the malpractice arena into a workers' compensation-like forum.

Private Contract

This approach, similar to a no-fault system, requires that patients and health care providers enter contractual agreements that explicitly provide the terms for resolving medical injury resulting from that care. An arbitration agreement is an example of such a contract. Parties may agree, however, on other forms of dispute resolution. For example, a patient may agree to waive the right to sue in return for a promise of compensation at a certain level should an adverse outcome occur. In essence, the health care provider would agree to insure the patient against the cost of medical injury.

This type of arrangement is common in commercial agreements where parties specify the exact amount of compensation (liquidated damages) to be received in event the other party fails to perform according to the terms of the contract, thus eliminating the need to litigate this issue.

No states have legislation addressing such contracts, nor would any legislation be necessary, since such agreements would be purely consensual arrangements on the part of the patient and health care provider. As contracts, the terms would be enforceable by courts. Certain types of contracts, such as ones where patients waive all rights to sue or those that appear to have been executed under duress or adhesion, have been held unenforceable as against public policy. Suspect contracts in health care, for example, would be those arranged before any treatment was begun or those contracts waiving rights to sue as a condition of receiving medical treatment.

Arbitration

Arbitration is a form of dispute resolution that is conducted privately by the parties to the dispute and impartial third party, who is often an expert in the area of controversy.

Generally, the decision is binding on the parties, although some arbitration procedures permit unsatisfied parties to seek subsequent judicial resolution of the dispute. There is little if any judicial review of the process. Arbitration is a common alternative dispute resolution (ADR) that has been used successfully for years in commercial and labor disputes. Because arbitration is less costly and faster than litigation in resolving claims and utilizes expert decision makers, some believe that arbitration offers benefits to both injured patients and health care providers. Others are wary of the private nature of the arbitration process and feel that this would reduce health care provider quality incentives.

Under most states' general arbitration statutes, medical malpractice claims can be resolved. During the 1970s, however, states began to enact specific statutes authorizing medical malpractice arbitration. Under arbitration, neutral third parties or panels resolve disputes. These decision makers usually operate with less formality than the courts, but the legal principle is the same—an injured party must prove that health care provider's negligence or fault caused the injury. Generally, parties to a dispute who choose arbitration for resolving claims do so voluntarily. However, as a condition of enrollment in the health care plan, some HMOs have mandated that members use arbitration to resolve claims.

In entering into contracts for medical services with patients, some HMOs mandate the use of arbitration with binding decisions for medical malpractice. Two such HMOs, Ross-Loos and Kaiser Permanente, require about 6.5 million subscribers to arbitrate claims arising from care received through health care plans. Ross-Loos, located in southern California, includes arbitration in all its contracts. Kaiser plans enroll about 6.5 million people in 16 states. While Kaiser includes mandatory arbitration in health care contracts in only five states, these plans cover about 85 percent of the total enrollees. All enrollees in the Ross-Loos and Kaiser health care plans, regardless of the source of payment for the coverage, are required to use arbitration if it is included in the health care contract.

The HMOs implemented this alternative for different reasons. When Ross-Loos began including mandatory arbitration in its contracts in the mid-1940s, medical malpractice was not a major concern. The HMO wanted to establish an ongoing relationship with its members and believed that resolving disputes through arbitration would be less adversarial and more private than the courts. Kaiser incorporated arbitration in the early 1970s as medical malpractice claims and costs were rising in California.

Plaintiffs in California challenged the legality of requiring members of health care plans to arbitrate claims and the constitutionality of waiving the right to jury trial without express consent. The California Supreme Court, however, found that such contracts were not illegal and did not violate the right to jury trial.

Arbitration offers several advantages for managed care providers and their members including faster claims resolution and lower defense costs, with more predictable and equitable results. The average arbitration takes about 19 months, compared with 33 months for litigated cases. Arbitration costs are lower primarily because of lower defense costs and a reduced likelihood of excessive awards. Finally, arbitration hearings require about 2 to 4 days, compared with several weeks for litigation.

Critics of arbitration say it may encourage small or nuisance claims and, because of its non-public nature, protect those at fault. They also feel that there is no real deterrent to medical negligence in this type of forum and that the overall costs of malpractice may increase if the filing of claims becomes easier.

CONCLUSION

As you can see, being named in a medical malpractice lawsuit may begin a long and draining process. As stated before, just because you are innocent of any wrongdoing does not mean that the plaintiff cannot name you in a lawsuit. You can defend yourself and prove that you were not negligent, but the process can be grueling. The best protection against any lawsuit is to keep your skills sharp and to always be professional and show sympathy to the patient's needs.

EXAM QUESTIONS

CHAPTER 7
Questions 78–91

78. What can you learn from reading a patient's complaint (lawsuit)?

    a. who is named in the suit and the grievances against you and others

    b. who is named in the suit and a detailed accounting of the claim of negligence

    c. the witnesses who will be called at trial

    d. the date of the trial

79. The statute of limitations may be extended if

    a. the patient could not afford a lawyer at the time of the incident.

    b. the patient was seriously injured as a result of a health care provider's negligence.

    c. the patient did not know that a health care provider had been negligent at the time of the incident.

    d. the patient lives in another state.

80. What should your first action be upon learning that you have been named in a medical malpractice lawsuit?

    a. hire a lawyer

    b. notify your state Board of Nursing

    c. call the plaintiff

    d. notify your insurance company, hospital attorney, or risk manager

81. What is the main purpose of discovery?

    a. for the plaintiff to learn why he or she was injured

    b. for the lawyers to learn as much about the case as possible

    c. for the defendants to learn if they were negligent

    d. for private investigators to stay in business

82. The period of discovery is the time when

    a. the plaintiff's injury occurred.

    b. the plaintiff discovered his injury.

    c. lawyers try to learn as much about the case as possible.

    d. all parties discover who was negligent.

83. Which of the following legal documents is frequently used during the period of discovery to gather information?

    a. summons

    b. complaint

    c. interrogatories

    d. res ipsa loquitur

84. What is the main purpose of depositions?

    a. to allow the lawyers to talk with the parties involved in the lawsuit

    b. to allow the defendants to state why they are innocent

    c. to allow the plaintiff to state how much money to settle for

    d. to relieve the court of an overload of cases

85. To prepare for a deposition, your lawyer may ask you to

    a. call and talk to the plaintiff.

    b. call and talk to the other defendants.

    c. review the patient's medical record.

    d. correct any errors in the medical record.

86. When answering questions on a deposition, you should

    a. refuse to answer unless otherwise instructed by your lawyer.

    b. be as instructional as possible.

    c. guess if you do not know the answer.

    d. answer as succinctly as possible.

87. The usual reason for settling a malpractice lawsuit before trial is

    a. when the insurance company thinks the defendants were negligent.

    b. when the insurance company does not think the defendants would make good witnesses.

    c. the insurance company feels sorry for the plaintiff.

    d. to avoid the expense of a trial.

88. When you testify at trial, you should

    a. refuse to answer any of the plaintiff's lawyers' questions.

    b. always speak to your lawyer.

    c. always speak to the jury.

    d. try to engender sympathy from the jury.

89. The role of the expert witness is to

    a. testify to what really happened.

    b. serve as an advocate for the plaintiff.

    c. explain the appropriate standard of care and pinpoint where the exact act of negligence occurred.

    d. assist the plaintiff's attorney in understanding the complex medical issues involved in the case.

90. The theory of enterprisal liability seeks to

    a. shift liability from individual providers to the facility at which they practiced.

    b. establish a no-fault mechanism for compensation.

    c. focus on policies and procedures of the enterprisal to explain the providers actions.

    d. force a defendant to find others who might also have responsibility for the plaintiffs injury.

91. Arbitration is a form of dispute resolution that

    a. mandates the use of a jury.

    b. uses physician experts to assist in understanding the complex medical issues.

    c. is available only to the uninsured.

    d. is conducted privately with the parties to the dispute and an impartial third party.

CHAPTER 8

EVALUATING YOUR NEED FOR MALPRACTICE INSURANCE

CHAPTER OBJECTIVE

After studying this chapter, the reader will be able to describe how personal liability insurance, and the laws that offer protection from liability, protect the nurse.

LEARNING OBJECTIVES

After reading this chapter, the reader will be able to

1. explain why having a personal liability insurance policy will not necessarily invite a medical malpractice lawsuit.

2. recognize the type of professional liability insurance policy that covers only claims reported while the policy is in force.

3. identify one type of situation that can cause a coverage dilemma under an occurrence policy.

4. define what is meant by the limits specified on a liability policy.

5. discuss the circumstances that would determine whether an insurance company would have to seek a nurse's approval before settling a case.

6. identify the type of damages that are awarded to punish the defendant for some act of gross negligence.

7. describe the type of damages which serve to punish the nurse for gross negligence.

8. explain the main purpose of the Good Samaritan Acts.

As much as you may not wish to admit it, you may one day be named in a medical malpractice lawsuit. As was discussed in the last chapter, the number of malpractice claims filed against nurses is rising. Even though a nurse accused of malpractice may be innocent, proving that fact can be expensive. Because of the risk that simply working as a nurse brings, you need to make sure that you're adequately protected, both by having insurance and by knowing the laws that protect you.

EVALUATING YOUR NEED FOR INSURANCE

Many nurses choose not to purchase professional liability insurance, feeling that having such a policy would simply make them more of a target for a lawsuit. They feel that if they do not have insurance, they will not get sued. But that is not true. In reality, most lawsuits are filed against nurses before the plaintiffs even know whether or not the nurse has insurance. In addition, once a case reaches trial, most states do not allow the lawyers to tell the jury whether or not the defendant has insurance. The reason for this rule is so the jury will return a judgment based on the facts of the case and not be swayed by whether an insurance company will be paying an award.

Another reason nurses often give for not purchasing an individual professional liability policy is that they feel they have all the coverage they need through their place of employment. Again, this may not be true. You may indeed have liability coverage through your employer; however, depending upon the policy and other circumstances, you may not be completely protected. It is important for you to know the conditions under which you are covered by your employer, then determine if you need separate individual coverage.

An employer is responsible for the acts of its employees under the doctrine of respondeat superior. However, if a hospital is found guilty of negligence because of some act or omission on your part, it has the option of suing you to recover the damages it paid. The chances of this happening might be slim, but you should know that it is a possibility. One situation where this occurred is detailed in the case of *Higley v. Florida Patient's Compensation Fund* (1988).

In this case, the mother of a male infant patient sued a hospital because of an incident that led to the death of her son. The nurse involved in the incident was not personally named in the lawsuit. However, it was her negligence that formed the basis of the lawsuit, and for which the plaintiffs were claiming the hospital was vicariously liable.

The hospital was a member of the Florida Patient's Compensation Fund, a fund that provides its member hospitals with unlimited coverage. Before the lawsuit reached trial, it was settled for $425,000. The Fund then turned around and filed suit against the nurse and her personal liability insurance company, claiming that it had a right to recover at least some of its money because the nurse was the one at fault. Both the Circuit Court and the District Court of Appeals agreed that the Fund had a right to recover the money. However, the Supreme Court of Florida disagreed. It stated that, because the nurse was a hospital employee, she was covered by the Fund. Because of that cov-

erage, the Fund could not seek to recover money from her because of the premise that an insurance company cannot sue its own insured.

This case turned out favorably for the nurse, but it had to go through the Circuit Court, the District Court of Appeals, and the Supreme Court before it did so. It is true that the case may never have evolved if the nurse did not have insurance; but it could have. Without insurance to cover the costs of all those trials, the results to the nurse could have been financially disastrous.

Another aspect to consider is the fact that your employer's policy only covers you while you are at work. If you ever volunteer your services at a health fair not sponsored by your employer, or even offer advice to a neighbor, you are assuming a risk for which you would not be covered under your employer's policy.

In addition, relying solely on your employer's coverage leaves you without any control over your insurance protection. For example, consider a situation in which the hospital you work for is financially troubled and, in an effort to save money, fails to pay its insurance premiums. As a result, you would be left without coverage. Furthermore, if your hospital does not cooperate with the insurance company during a lawsuit, or if it misrepresented its situation when it applied for the policy, the insurance company could refuse to cover the hospital, and, in turn, you. Not only could you be left totally without coverage, you may not even know it until you are in the midst of a lawsuit.

Another thing to consider regarding your employer's coverage is the policy itself. Most policies may contain exclusions for which it will not offer coverage. Exclusions vary widely between policies, but the insurance company may refuse to cover certain acts, situations, or even certain employees. Because the scope of nursing practice is expanding, your hospital's policy may not provide the coverage you need for all of your activities.

Hospitals may also refuse to protect you if you acted beyond what is described in your hospital's policy and procedure manual. This is true even if it is common knowledge that the existing policies do not accurately reflect what nurses are doing.

To adequately evaluate your need for additional insurance, you first need to know the details of the insurance policy that your employer provides. Request a copy of the policy and then evaluate it thoroughly. Better yet, ask a professional liability insurance agent to review it. Most agents will be happy to perform such a service, free of charge, just for the opportunity of talking to you about the exclusions and limits of your employer's policy.

Once you know the limits of your employer's policy, carefully evaluate your own nursing practice for areas that may not be adequately protected by your employer's policy. For example, do you work in a specialized setting, such as intensive care or the delivery room? Do you function in an expanded nursing role, such as nurse practitioner or community health nurse? If so, not only is your risk of being sued higher than average, you may be routinely performing functions that your employer's policy may not cover. In addition, you may wish to become an advocate for redrafting your hospital's policies and procedures to accurately reflect the tasks you perform.

CHOOSING YOUR POLICY

Once you have determined that purchasing additional insurance would be a good idea, you need to decide the type of policy best for you.

Selecting the Type of Policy

The two basic types of policies are claims-made policies and occurrence policies. The majority of all professional liability insurance policies written for nurses are claims-made policies. However, so that you can better evaluate any pol-

icy presented to you, it is important for you to understand the basic differences between these two policies.

Claims-made policies cover claims reported while the policy is in force. For example, say you purchase a policy for the term from June 2001 through May 2002. Basically, any allegation of negligence made against you between these two dates would be covered under the policy. The incident in question may have occurred **before** the policy was in force, but as long as the claim was not made until after the policy was effective, it would be covered.

An exception to this occurs with new policies. Usually, when a policy is written, it carries what is called a retro date. If the policy is written on May 2, 2001, the retro date will most likely be May 2, 2001. The policy will then cover any incident that occurs after that date. If you renew the same policy the next year, the retro date will still be May 2. Therefore, the longer you have the policy, the more years will be covered under the policy.

Another exception to the period of time covered by a policy occurs if you know about an incident but intentionally do not inform the insurance company. Insurance companies define the term claim fairly broadly. In addition to a filed lawsuit, insurance companies consider several other situations to constitute a claim. For example, if a patient or his lawyer makes a charge of negligence, if a patient threatens to sue, or if you know that you may have injured a patient through some act of negligence, then the insurance company might consider a claim to have been made when you file the report with the company. Many insurers produce a list of eight to ten serious patient injuries; when one of these injuries occurs, and the injury is reported, then the insurance company considers a claim to have been made. It is not necessary for a lawsuit to have been filed for an incident to be covered by a claims-made policy. All that is necessary is that both you and the insurance company are aware of a situation that may result in a lawsuit. The claims-made policy would offer coverage under this type of scenario.

The other type of insurance is an **occurrence policy.** This type of policy is usually written only for hospitals, but occasionally it may be available to nurses. Instead of focusing on the date of the claim, this type of policy focuses on the date that the incident occurred. If the policy you purchase for the term of June 2001 through May 2002 is an occurrence policy, then the policy would cover you for any alleged acts of negligence that occurred during that time span. It does not matter if neither you nor the insurance company have any knowledge that the patient plans to sue. As long as the incident in question occurred during the policy period, you would be covered, even if the patient does not make a claim until years after the policy ends. As a general rule, claims-made policies are cheaper than occurrence policies. This is because, with a claims-made policy, the insurance company is at risk only for the duration of the policy. Once the policy lapses, the insurance company has no obligation to cover you in the event of a lawsuit. With an occurrence policy, the insurance company is at risk for providing coverage for years after the policy ends.

While neither policy is better than the other, claims-made policies can present a problem if you retire or leave the practice of nursing and you let your policy lapse. As of that moment, you would no longer be covered. Because lawsuits can be filed years after the incident in question, you could be in a financially vulnerable situation. Another problem would occur if you, or your employer, switched from a claims-made policy to an occurrence policy. Since the claims-made policy would no longer offer coverage from the moment the policy lapsed, and the occurrence policy would only offer coverage for incidents that occurred during its policy period, you could have a gap in coverage.

Because of this gap, insurance companies offer an extended reporting endorsement, or "tail coverage," which would maintain your coverage under the claims-made policy. Although these policies tend to be expensive, you should always purchase such a supplemental policy if you have ever had a claims-made policy and decide to change the policy for some reason. A situation where a nurse did not purchase such coverage, and was caught off guard, is described in the case of *William M. Mercer, Inc. v. Woods* (1978).

In this instance, a nurse anesthetist worked at a Texas hospital. On February 8, 1978, she administered anesthesia to a patient who was giving birth. Because of the anesthesia, the patient suffered complications and later died. The patient's family sued, and the nurse was found to have been negligent. The court entered a judgment against her in the amount of $1,209,000 plus post-judgment interest and costs.

More problems arose because her liability insurance changed from a claims-made policy to an occurrence policy on April 1, 1978. Because the incident in question occurred in February, the occurrence policy refused coverage. And, because she had not notified her insurance company when the incident occurred—thus making them aware of a possible claim—the claims-made policy also refused coverage. As a result, the nurse was totally without coverage for both her defense and the $1.2 million judgment.

As it turned out, the nurse had made an attempt to buy tail coverage but, because of some deception on the part of her insurance company, the application had not been accepted. She was then able to sue the insurance company for deceptive trade practice. Regardless, this case illustrates the predicament you could end up in if you fail to buy tail coverage after having had a claims-made policy.

On the other hand, occurrence policies can present their own problems. The main difficulty can occur if it is not clear exactly when the incident occurred. For example, say that you are a nurse practitioner and that you have been treating a patient for several months for gastrointestinal upset. You feel that the patient's problem is stress related, and you have been treating the problem accordingly by prescribing antacids and by counseling the patient on stress-reduction techniques and dietary changes. Because the problem has not improved, you finally refer the patient to a gastroenterologist. After several tests, the doctor diagnoses the patient as having stomach cancer. As a result, the patient sues you for having failed to refer them to a doctor.

In this instance, when did the "incident" occur? If the several months that you treated the patient occurred both inside and outside of the policy period, the insurance company could question whether you are actually covered.

Setting the Limits

Once you have determined the type of policy you want, you need to consider the dollar amount of the coverage. Every policy has a limit, which is the amount of money that the insurance company will pay if you are found liable and ordered to pay damages.

Most policy limits are listed as a combination number; for example, $1,000,000/$3,000,000. For this policy, $1,000,000 is the maximum amount of money that the insurance company will pay on any one claim. This amount applies whether the money is paid as a settlement or to honor a judgment. In addition, the $1,000,000 limit applies regardless of the number of parties filing suit on the same charge. For example, imagine that you have been found solely negligent for causing a patient's injury. The patient is awarded $900,000 in damages, and his wife, who has joined him in the lawsuit, is awarded $500,000 for loss of consortium. Regardless of the fact that the lawsuit involves two parties who have each received an award, the insur-

ance company will still pay only $1 million total. You would then be personally responsible for the excess judgment of $400,000.

The $3 million limit is what is known as the aggregate. This is the total limit of the money that the insurance company will pay out in settlements and judgments during the policy period. However, there is no limit on the number of lawsuits against which the insurance company will defend you. If you are sued four times in the same year, the insurance company will defend you each time, regardless of the expense involved. However, it will only pay out settlements or judgments until the $3 million aggregate is exhausted.

Despite the example given above, it is rare that a nurse would be found solely liable and ordered to pay a $1.4 million judgment. Generally speaking, you could feel secure with a policy limit of $1 million and relieve some worry about your own assets being at risk.

Although it may sound as if having a $1 million insurance policy would be outrageously expensive, that actually is not the case. The premiums for a policy with such a limit would not be much more than for a policy with a much lower limit. Because the insurance company has already assumed a certain risk by offering the policy, a higher limit would not increase the premium disproportionately. Many nursing organizations offer group professional liability insurance at surprisingly low rates.

Tailoring the Policy to Your Needs

When selecting an insurance policy, you also need to evaluate the features of the policy in light of your particular nursing practice. For example, if you frequently supervise other nurses, you would want to make sure that the policy would cover you if you are named in a lawsuit as a result of the negligence of one of those nurses. Also, would the policy cover you if a patient is injured because you misused a piece of equipment or made a mistake when reporting or recording the patient's care? What about if you failed to teach a patient, made a mistake when administering a medication, or were accused of libel or slander? You would also want to verify that the policy would cover you in case the hospital sued you, and that it would also cover you for any professional services you perform outside your employment setting. Another aspect you may wish to look at is if the insurance company will reimburse you for any expenses you incur, or any salary you lose, while participating in the defense of a lawsuit.

When evaluating various policies, it would be a good idea to work with an agent who has experience handling professional liability insurance. This way, you can describe your practice and precisely list your responsibilities to the agent, who can identify the features you need in a policy. If you do not know how to find such an insurance agent, call a local nursing organization for guidance.

Depending upon the type of coverage you have through your employer, you may choose a policy that covers specific areas and supplements the general policy you have through your employer. On the other hand, you may decide to purchase a policy that provides coverage over and above that provided by your employer's policy. Either way, just be sure to complete the application as accurately as possible. Remember, if you misrepresent anything on the application, the insurance company can later refuse to honor the coverage.

WHAT THE INSURANCE COMPANY AGREES TO OFFER

In return for your purchasing a policy, an insurance company agrees to defend you if you are ever accused of negligence. This is one of the most important aspects of having liability insurance. As has already been stated, defending your-

self—whether you are guilty or not—can be very expensive.

As part of your defense, the insurance company will hire a lawyer to defend you. Most insurance companies reserve the right to choose the lawyer who will represent you. But you can rest assured that the lawyer will be a good one. The insurance company does not want to pay out any more money than it has to; therefore, the lawyer assigned to you will most likely be someone highly experienced in defending malpractice lawsuits. Besides paying the attorney's fees, the insurance company will pay what's necessary to investigate the circumstances surrounding the incident, to obtain expert witnesses, and for any necessary exhibits, such as photographs, posters, or other visual aids.

Although the lawyer hired by the insurance company is representing your interests, you have no say regarding legal tactics and strategy. This is left up to the lawyer and the insurance company to determine. If you do not feel that the lawyer is providing you with proper representation, or if you feel that the lawyer is placing the interests of the insurance company above your own, then you need to put those complaints in writing and mail them to your representative at the insurance company.

Many times, the insurance company will actively try to settle the case, especially if the cost of settlement will be less than the cost of defending the case. Most medical malpractice cases are long and drawn out, and lawyers' fees are high; trying such a case can be costly indeed. Many times, early in the lawsuit, plaintiffs are willing to settle for an amount of money less than the amount required to defend the case. Therefore, settling a case is often the least expensive route.

In addition, insurance companies know the uncertainties involved in trying a case before a jury. All insurance companies have seen judgments entered against defendants who were not negligent.

To understand how this can happen, first consider how complicated the situation surrounding a claim of malpractice can be. Next, consider how difficult it is to separate emotion from the facts when considering a patient's injury. With this in mind, it is easy to see how a jury could find for the plaintiff even though the defendant had not actually been negligent.

Another aspect that motivates insurance companies to settle cases is that if it refuses to accept a reasonable settlement offer, and a judgment is later entered against the insured person, then the company may have to pay the full judgment, even if the judgment exceeds the limits of the policy. Of course, whether the offer was reasonable or not depends upon a number of factors. For example, the court would want to know if the insurance company considered the interests of the insured as well as its own. The court would also investigate whether the insurance company thoroughly investigated the case and whether it appropriately and realistically evaluated the plaintiff's injuries.

If a claim is completely without merit, or the plaintiff's demand is disproportionate to the injury, the insurance company may choose to fight. However, depending upon the details of your policy, the insurance company may not have to consult you either way. If it wants to settle, it may usually do so without your consent, and without even letting you know.

Some policies, though, require the insurer to obtain your consent before settling a case. While this looks good on the surface, it actually places a greater responsibility on you. If you reject a settlement offer, and the jury returns a verdict in favor of the plaintiff for an amount greater than the settlement offer, then the insurance company may be able to limit the amount it pays to the settlement offer. Consider this example. You have been sued for malpractice. The patient's attorney has contacted your insurance company and has said that

$150,000 would settle the case. Your insurance company is inclined to go along with the settlement offer, but, under the terms of your policy, contacts you for permission to settle. You feel that the patient's claims of injury are inflated, and, furthermore, you feel that you were not negligent. Not wanting to admit any wrongdoing, you reject the offer. But, at trial, the jury finds in favor of the plaintiff and awards damages in the amount of $200,000. Since the plaintiff originally demanded only $150,000, it is possible that you would be responsible for paying the additional $50,000.

Whether an insurer must obtain your consent for a settlement depends on whether the policy contains a threshold limit. This limit is the amount of money over which the insurer must obtain your consent to settle. For example, if the threshold limit is $5,000, then the insurer can settle a case for less than that amount without consulting you, but it must obtain your permission to settle a case for more than that amount. Usually, a hospital's liability policy contains a threshold limit so that the hospital can retain some control over which cases are settled. If your policy has no threshold limit, then the insurance company can settle a case without your permission.

Throughout the course of its investigation—before either a settlement or a trial occurs—if the insurance company learns that there is a possibility that a judgment may be entered against you that exceeds your policy limits, then the insurance company has an additional obligation. It must investigate the situation further, and make an honest evaluation of whether this may, in fact, occur. Then, the insurance company must let you know both the facts learned in its investigation and its evaluation of the situation.

If your case does go to trial, and a judgment is entered against you, whether or not your insurance company is obligated to appeal depends upon the terms of your policy. For the most part, the insurance company is not obligated to finance an appeal.

YOUR OBLIGATIONS TO THE INSURANCE COMPANY

In addition to your insurance company's obligations to you, you, in turn, have certain obligations to the insurance company. Your first obligation is to be meticulously honest when completing your application for insurance. A nurse may be tempted to alter the truth to try and get a cheaper insurance rate: for example, she might falsely state that she has received specialized training, or wrongly claim that she has never been named in a malpractice lawsuit. However, if the insurance company relies on any of this false information when making its decision as to whether or not to offer you a policy, and later discovers the truth, the company could legally refuse to honor your coverage. Keep in mind that, if you are ever named in a lawsuit, the insurance company will scrutinize your application for any information that's not completely true.

Your next, and perhaps most important, obligation is to promptly notify the insurance company of any hint of a lawsuit. Besides being served with lawsuit papers, you might become aware of a possible claim in other ways. For example, imagine that you are administering an injection when you accidentally injure the patient's sciatic nerve. While the focus of your attention will be on seeing that the patient receives the care she or he needs, you should also realize that this is exactly the type of situation that could give rise to a lawsuit. Acting accordingly, you should notify your insurance company as soon as possible. You should also notify your insurance company if a patient threatens to sue, or if you become aware of a patient's lawyer making inquiries. It is better to inform the insurance company of a situation that never develops into a lawsuit

than not to tell the insurance company, only to find yourself named in a lawsuit for which your insurance company is refusing coverage.

While notifying the insurance company of a possible claim is particularly important with claims-made policies, most policies have some provision whereby you're obligated to let them know, in a timely manner, about all possible claims. And if you have more than one policy—such as your own policy in addition to that offered by your employer—you must inform each company.

LIMITATIONS OF LIABILITY INSURANCE

While specific limitations of liability coverage vary between policies, most policies contain certain general exclusions. For example, most insurance companies will refuse to honor coverage if a malpractice lawsuit results because a nurse violated a criminal statute or ordinance. Although this may seem like a remote possibility as far as nursing practice goes, it is not. For example, a nurse may be accused of the crime of false imprisonment. This charge may result if a nurse restrains a patient without sufficient cause. However, unless a nurse commits this act on purpose, or intentionally tries to harm the patient, most policies will still provide coverage.

Another instance for which most policies will refuse to honor coverage is if a nurse acts outside the scope of the state nurse practice act and injures a patient. This is one more reason for you to be aware of the parameters of your state's nurse practice act, and to always make sure that your care falls within those parameters.

Finally, many policies refuse to pay punitive damages if they are awarded. Remember, punitive damages are those damages that are awarded to punish the defendant for some act of gross negligence. These damages are different from compensatory damages, which the insurance will pay under the terms of the policy.

PROTECTION OFFERED BY THE LAW

Although it is still a good idea to have insurance, you need to know that the law does offer a certain amount of protection if you are accused of negligence for nursing services you perform away from your place of employment. First of all, the common law—which is based upon past court decisions—helps protect you when you offer your services in an emergency situation. The courts have an interest in protecting health care professionals when they help out in an emergency; after all, the courts do not want doctors and nurses turning their backs on accident victims because they're afraid of being sued.

As you will recall from Chapter 1, to support a claim of malpractice, a plaintiff must prove that you owed the plaintiff a duty, that you breached that duty, and that the result was injury. Proving duty would be perhaps the easiest part of the case; proving the rest would be much more difficult.

Although the law in most states does not require you to stop at an accident scene, you may choose to do so because of your own sense of morals and ethics. If you do stop at the scene of an accident, you have immediately established a nurse-patient relationship with the victim. As of that point, you cannot leave the victim until competent help arrives to take over.

Once you have established a duty, you have an obligation to deliver the same standard of care that a reasonable and prudent nurse would deliver under similar circumstances. If, for some reason, the victim later claims that you did not, he would have to prove harm as a result. Since the victim was injured to begin with, this could be difficult. As you may imagine, it would be difficult to determine what

portion of an injury occurred because of the accident, and what portion occurred because of the rescuer's negligence. To prove a case, most courts require the victim to prove that at least half of the injury resulted because of the rescuer's negligence.

But you do not have to rely on the fact that it would be difficult for the victim to prove all of these factors in a lawsuit. Most states have tried to protect rescuers even further by enacting a group of laws known as the Good Samaritan Acts. These laws specifically protect health care professionals from liability when they offer their services during an emergency. Of course, the acts would not protect you if you were to perform some grossly negligent act, but they will protect you from what would be considered "ordinary" negligence. If necessary, a jury would determine whether or not an act was ordinary negligence. The Good Samaritan Acts also will not protect you if you accept money for your services; the laws protect only those who donate their services.

Each state has its own version of the Good Samaritan Acts, and you should check with your local nursing organization for details on your state's laws. For example, the acts of some states cover any person, while others only apply to in-state nurses; some offer protection for failure to arrange for further medical treatment, and some do not.

Basically, though, victims rarely sue the person who tries to help in an emergency. In fact, there is no case where a nurse has had to defend himself or herself on the basis of being a "Good Samaritan." Just remember, if you do offer assistance in an emergency, take care to deliver the best care possible, just as you would in any other situation. Focus your attention on maintaining an airway, stopping bleeding, and assessing for fractures or other injuries. And, of course, stay with the victim until someone who is at least as skilled as you are arrives to assume care or to transfer the patient to a hospital.

CONCLUSION

In conclusion, your best protection against being sued is to make sure that the care you give is up to acceptable standards. But, given the fact that mistakes can happen, it is a good idea to be aware of your responsibilities under the law, and to make sure you have adequate insurance coverage.

EXAM QUESTIONS

CHAPTER 8

Questions 92–100

92. Although many nurses believe that having a professional liability policy invites lawsuits, this is not necessarily so because

    a. insurance companies do not become involved in lawsuits.

    b. insurance will not pay if a nurse has been negligent.

    c. most lawsuits are filed before the plaintiff knows if the defendant has insurance.

    d. courts allow the jury to know if the defendant has insurance.

93. What type of professional liability insurance policy covers only claims reported while the policy is in force?

    a. limits

    b. basic-choice

    c. occurrence

    d. claims-made

94. What is the main difficulty that can arise with an occurrence policy?

    a. Coverage is difficult to determine if there is no clear date of the incident.

    b. The amount of coverage depends on how soon the report is made.

    c. Coverage of claims are usually harder to collect with these policies.

    d. The policy covers only one occurrence of malpractice every 2 years.

95. What is meant by professional liability policy limits of $1,000,000/$3,000,000?

    a. $1,000,000 is the amount the policy will pay per person making a claim; $3,000,000 is the total amount the policy will pay per claim.

    b. $1,000,000 is the amount the insurance company will pay to try the case; $3,000,000 is the maximum amount the insurance company will pay in damages.

    c. $1,000,000 is the maximum amount the insurance company will pay to settle a case; $3,000,000 is the amount the company will pay if the damages are awarded by a jury.

    d. $1,000,000 is the maximum amount the insurance company will pay on any one claim; $3,000,000 is the maximum amount the insurance company will pay during the policy period on any number of claims.

96. If a nurse purchases an individual professional liability insurance policy, the insurance company agrees to pay which of the following if the nurse is sued?

    a. defense costs only

    b. a judgment if awarded, but not defense costs

    c. only the settlement

    d. all costs, including defense costs and a judgment or settlement

97. When does the insurance company have to get your approval to settle?

    a. anytime a settlement offer is made
    b. when you do not trust the lawyer the company assigned
    c. if the court orders the insurance company to settle
    d. if your policy contains a threshold limit

98. What type of damages are awarded to punish the defendant for some act of gross negligence?

    a. punitive
    b. compensatory
    c. threshold
    d. aggregate

99. An insurance company can refuse to honor coverage under a professional liability policy if a nurse

    a. was negligent.
    b. has more than one policy.
    c. acted outside the scope of the nurse practice acts.
    d. purchased tail coverage.

100. The main purpose of the Good Samaritan Acts is to

    a. force people to stop at an accident scene.
    b. protect those who offer help in emergencies.
    c. protect accident victims.
    d. relieve the hospital of liability.

This concludes the final examination. An answer key will be sent with your certificate so that you can determine which of your answers were correct and incorrect.

COURT CASES INDEX

In re Roe, 421 N.E. 2d 40 (Mass. 1981).

Salas v. Wang, 846 F.2d 897 (3rd Cir. 1988).

Sandhofer v. Abbot Northwestern Hosp., 283 N.W. 2d 362 (Minn. 1979).

Scaria v. St. Paul Fire & Marine Ins., 227 N.W. 2d 647 (Wis. 1975).

Seymour v. Victory Mem'l Hosp., 376 N.E. 2d 754 (Ill. App. Ct. 1978).

Shepard v. Kinbrough, 318 S.E. 2d 573.

Slatkin v. Capitol Hill Hosp., No. 84-0443 (D.C. Oct. 18, 1984).

Smelko v. Brinton, 740 P.2d 591 (Kan. 1987).

Smith v. West Calcasieu-Cameron Hosp., 251 So. 2d 810 (La. 1971).

Spring, Earl, Unreported opinion cited by Jack Horsley, E.J.P., *RN,* Sept. 1983.

St. Elizabeth Hosp. v. Graham, 883 S.W. 2d 433 (Tex. 1994).

Stevenson v. Alta Bates, 66 P. 2d 1265 (Cal. Ct. App. 1937).

Story v. St. Mary District, Unpublished district court decision, 1987.

Striano v. Deepdale Gen. Hosp., 387 N.Y.S. 2d 678 (1976).

Sullivan v. Sumrall, 618 So. 2d 1274 (Miss. 1993).

Tarasoff v. Regents of the Univ. of Cal., 551 P.2d 334 (Cal. 1976).

Truhitte v. French Hosp., 128 Cal. App. 3d 332 (5th Dist 1982).

Tuma v. Board of Nursing, 593 P.2d 711 (Idaho 1979).

Utter v. United Hosp. Ctr., 236 S.E. 2d 213 (W. Va. 1977).

Variety Children's Hosp. v. Perkins, 382 So. 2d 331 (Fla. 1980).

Vodopest v. MacGregor, 913 P.2d 779 (Wash. 1996).

Von Stetina v. Florida Med. Ctr., 436 So. 2d 1022 (Fla. 1983).

Wood v. Miller, 76 P.2d 963 (Ore. 1938).

Woods v. William M. Mercer, Inc., 717 S.W. 2d 391 (Tex. App. 1986).

Ybarra v. Spangard, 208 P.2d 445 (Cal. Ct. App. 1944).

BIBLIOGRAPHY

Allen, J., Herron, D., Rajki, M., Sykora, B. & Kelley, S. (2000). Legal Documentation. A Case Study in Basic Concepts. *Advanced Nurse Practitioner, 8*(1), 67–68.

Austin, S. (2000). What's your liability in a survey? *Nursing Management, 31*(2),14.

Baker, S.K. (2000). Minimizing litigation risk. Documentation strategies in the occupational health setting. *American Association of Occupational Health Nursing Journal, 48*(2), 100-5; quiz 106–7.

Blumenreich, G. A. (1999). Litigation is too important to be entrusted to lawyers. *American Association of Nurse Attorneys Journal, 67*(4), 311–4.

Blumenreich, G. A. (1999). Significance of signing medical chart on legal liability. *American Association of Nurse Attorneys Journal, 67*(1), 13–6.

Brown, S. M. (1999). Good Samaritan laws: Protection and limits. *RN, 62*(11), 65–8.

Cady, R. (2000). So you want to be an expert witness? Things you need to know. *American Journal of Maternal Child Nursing, 25*(1), 49.

Coombes, R. (1999). Forwarned is forearmed, *Nursing Times, 95*(36), 12–3.

Fiesta, J. (1999). Nursing Malpractice: Cause for consideration. *Nursing Management, 30*(2), 12–3.

Fiesta, J. (1999). When sexual harassment hits home. *Nursing Management, 30*(5), 16–8.

Fiesta, J. (1999). Who's liable in equipment cases? *Nursing Management, 30*(4), 12–3,15.

Frank-Stromborg, M. & Christiansen, A. (2000). The undertreatment of pain: A liability risk for nurses. *Clinial Journal of Oncology Nursing, 4*(1), 41–4.

Gondringer N. S. (1999). Deposition: Never underestimate its significance. *American Association of Nurse Attorneys Journal, 67*(3), 221–3.

Health Care Financing Administration. (July 2, 1999). *Federal Register, 64*, 27, p. 36078.

Henrickson, T. (2000). Re: "Telephone triage and consultation: An emerging role for nurses," *Nursing Outlook, 48*(2), 92–3.

LaDuke, S. (2000). What should you expect from your attorney? *Nursing Management, 31*(1), 10.

Mahlmeister, L. (1999). Professional accountability and legal liability for the team leader and charge nurse. *Journal of Obstetric, Gynecologic and Neonatal Nursing, 28*(3), 300–9.

Meiner, S. E. (1999). Delegation can be miscalculated. *Geriatric Nursing, 20*(2), 100,105.

Morrison, C. A. (1999). A malpractice primer for NPs. *Advanced Nurse Practitioner, 7*(2), 23.

Morrison, C. A. (1999). Evolving legal trends affect NPs. *Advanced Nurse Practitioner, 7*(5), 24.

Morrison, C. A. (1999). Understanding a civil trial. *Advanced Nurse Practitioner, 7*(8), 25.

Murphy, E. K. (2000). New roles and new twists on old roles. *Association of Operating Room Nurses Journal, 71*(1), 209–11.

Nurse's Legal Handbook, 3rd edition. Springhouse, Pa., Springhouse Corp., 1996.

Otto, D. A. (1999). Regulatory statutes and issues-clinical accountability in perioperative settings. *Association of Operating Room Nurses Journal, 70*(2), 241–4, 246–7, 249–52.

Phillips, E. (1999). Managing risks in obstetrical nursing. *Canadian Nurse, 95*(1), 45–6.

Sheehy, S. B. (1999). Understanding the legal process: Your best defense. *Journal of Emergency Nursing, 25*(6), 492–5.

Showers, J. L. (1999). Protection from negligence lawsuits. *Nursing Management, 30*(9), 23–7; quiz 28.

SELECTED WEB SITES

American Association of Nurse Attorneys: http://www.taana.org

American Health Lawyers Association: http://www.healthlawyers.org

Nurses Service organization: http://www.nso.com

NursingNet: http://www.nursingnet.org

INDEX

PRETEST KEY

1.   b   Chapter 1
2.   c   Chapter 1
3.   a   Chapter 1
4.   d   Chapter 1
5.   c   Chapter 2
6.   a   Chapter 2
7.   c   Chapter 3
8.   d   Chapter 3
9.   d   Chapter 3
10.   a   Chapter 3
11.   c   Chapter 4
12.   b   Chapter 4
13.   b   Chapter 4
14.   b   Chapter 5
15.   b   Chapter 5
16.   a   Chapter 6
17.   a   Chapter 6
18.   b   Chapter 6
19.   c   Chapter 6
20.   b   Chapter 6

NOTES

Western Schools® offers over 60 topics to suit all your interests – and requirements!

Clinical Conditions/Nursing Practice

A Nurse's Guide to Weight Control for Healthy Living..................................25 hrs

Airway Management with a Tracheal Tube ....1 hr

Auscultation Skills: Breath and Heart Sounds ......12 hrs

Basic Nursing of Head, Chest, Abdominal, Spine and Orthopedic Trauma ....16 hrs

Care at the End of Life................................3 hrs

Chest Tube Management ....2 hrs

Death, Dying & Bereavement ....30 hrs

Diabetes Nursing Care ....30 hrs

Healing Nutrition ....24 hrs

Hepatitis C: The Silent Killer ....2 hrs

HIV/AIDS...1, 2, 4 or 30 hrs

Holistic & Complementary Therapies: Introduction..1 hr

Managing Obesity and Eating Disorders ....30 hrs

Nursing Care of the HIV-Infected Patient..............30 hrs

Orthopedic Nursing: Caring for Patients with Musculoskeletal Disorders ....30 hrs

Pain Management: Principles and Practice............30 hrs

The Neurological Exam...1 hr

Wound Management and Healing...........................30 hrs

Cosmetic Treatments/Surgery

Belt Lipectomy: Lower Body Contouring ....1 hr

Botox Treatments and Dermal Fillers.......................1 hr

Cosmetic Breast Surgery ....1 hr

Weight Loss Surgery ....1 hr

Critical Care/ER/OR

Ambulatory Surgical Care ....20 hrs

Case Studies in Critical Care Nursing: A Guide for Application and Review ....46 hrs

Principles of Basic Trauma Nursing ....30 hrs

Geriatrics

Alzheimer's Disease: A Complete Guide for Nurses ..25 hrs

Alzheimer's: Things a Nurse Needs to Know........12 hrs

Elder Abuse ....4 hrs

Home Health Nursing ....30 hrs

Nursing Care of the Older Adult ....30 hrs

Psychosocial Issues Affecting Older Adults ....16 hrs

For our free catalog, visit our website www.westernschools.com or call today!
1-800-438-8888

Infectious Diseases/Bioterrorism

Biological Weapons ....5 hrs

Bioterrorism & the Nurse's Response to WMD ......5 hrs

Bioterrorism Readiness: The Nurse's Critical Role .. 2 hrs

Infection Control Training for Healthcare Workers ..4 hrs

Influenza: A Vaccine-Preventable Disease ....1 hr

SARS: An Emerging Public Health Threat ....1 hr

Smallpox...2 hrs

The New Threat of Drug Resistant Microbes ....5 hrs

West Nile Virus ....1 hr

Oncology

Cancer in Women..30 hrs

Cancer Nursing: A Solid Foundation for Practice ..30 hrs

Chemotherapy Essentials: Principles & Practice ..15 hrs

Pediatrics/Maternal-Child/Women's Health

Attention Deficit Hyperactivity Disorders Throughout the Lifespan..................................30 hrs

Diabetes in Children ....30 hrs

End-of-Life Care for Children and Their Families ....2 hrs

Manual of School Health...30 hrs

Maternal-Newborn Nursing....................................30 hrs

Menopause: Nursing Care for Women Throughout Mid-Life ....25 hrs

Pediatric Nursing: Routine to Emergent Care........30 hrs

Pediatric Pharmacology ....10 hrs

Pediatric Physical Assessment...............................10 hrs

Women's Health: Contemporary Advances and Trends ....30 hrs

Professional Issues/Management/Law

Medical Error Prevention: Patient Safety ....2 hrs

Nursing Practice and the Law ....30 hrs

Nursing and Malpractice Risks: Understanding the Law ....30 hrs

Ohio Law: Standards of Safe Nursing Practice ....1 hr

Supervisory Skills for Nurses ....30 hrs

Surviving and Thriving in Nursing ....30 hrs

Understanding Managed Care.................................30 hrs

Psychiatric/Mental Health

Antidepressants ....1 hr

Antipsychotics ....1 hr

Anxiolytics and Mood Stabilizers.............................1 hr

Basic Psychopharmacology......................................5 hrs

IPV (Intimate Partner Violence): A Domestic Violence Concern ....1 or 3 hrs

Psychiatric Principles & Applications for General Patient Care ....30 hrs

Psychiatric Nursing: Current Trends in Diagnosis and Treatment ....30 hrs

Substance Abuse ....30 hrs

Visit us online at www.westernschools.com for these great courses – plus all the latest CE topics!
Online testing also available.

REV. 1/28/05